CW00552362

# Access to Anaesthetics Primary FRCA Pocket Book 3: Physiology and Anatomy MCQs

**Kirsty MacLennan MBChB, MRCP, FRCA**

Specialist Registrar Anaesthesia

North West Region

PasTest
Dedicated to your success

© 2007 PASTEST LTD
Egerton Court
Parkgate Estate
Knutsford
Cheshire
WA16 8DX

Telephone: 01565 752000

First Published 2007

ISBN: 1905 635 311
ISBN: 978 1905 635 313

A catalogue record for this book is available from the British Library.

The information contained within this book was obtained by the author from reliable sources. However, while every effort has been made to ensure its accuracy, no responsibility for loss, damage or injury occasioned to any person acting or refraining from action because of information contained herein can be accepted by the publishers or author.

---

**PasTest Revision Books and Intensive Courses**

PasTest has been established in the field of postgraduate medical education since 1972, providing revision books and intensive study courses for doctors preparing for their professional examinations.

Books and courses are available for the following specialties:
MRCGP, MRCP Parts 1 and 2, MRCPCH Parts 1 and 2, MRCPsych, MRCS, MRCOG Parts 1 and 2, DRCOG, DCH, FRCA, PLAB Parts 1 and 2.

For further details contact:
PasTest, Freepost, Knutsford, Cheshire WA16 7BR
**Tel: 01565 752000 Fax: 01565 650264**
**www.pastest.co.uk enquiries@pastest.co.uk**

---

Typeset by Keytec Typesetting Ltd, Bridport, UK
Printed and bound in the UK by Athenaeum Press, Gateshead

# CONTENTS

# ACKNOWLEDGEMENTS

I would like to thank Dr. Nolan for taking the time to write the foreword; Dr. Whitaker for his review; Dr. S. Maguire, Dr. K. Grady and Dr. W. de Mello for their advice and encouragement.

I would also like to thank the publishers, PasTest, my family, who have supported me. And above all, Ann MacLennan who has been my rock as always!

# FOREWORD

The introduction of run-through training in Anaesthesia and the need for the Royal College of Anaesthetists [RCOA] to structure timing and content of Postgraduate examinations in accordance with the requirements of the Postgraduate Medical and Education Training Board [PMETB] has led to recent changes to the Primary Fellowship of the Royal College of Anaesthetists [FRCA] examination.

The Primary Multiple Choice Question [MCQ] examination became a "stand alone" Pass/Fail examination in June 2007. A close marking scheme is used where 1 is a poor fail, 1+ is a fail, 2 is a Pass and a 2+ reflects an outstanding performance. The Primary FRCA MCQ examination consists of 90 questions undertaken in three hours and comprises three subsections of 30 MCQs examining Pharmacology, Physiology, Physics and Clinical Measurement. A mark of 2 is required to pass the MCQ although a candidate who significantly underperforms in one or more subsection of the MCQ will fail the examination. Negative marking is applied with one mark being deducted for each incorrect answer.

A candidate may not proceed to the Objectively Structured Clinical Examination/Structured Oral Examination part of the Primary without passing the MCQ. An MCQ pass will be valid for a period of three years for a trainee working full time.

Although there is currently no limit on the number of attempts at this part of the examination, implicit in run through training is the need for trainees to achieve clinical competencies and examination milestones in a timely fashion.

It is generally acknowledged that an MCQ examination is a good test of core knowledge and there is no short cut to the acquisition of the considerable amount of information required to pass the Primary MCQ. Prospective candidates need to commit to an intensive programme of study of the syllabus supported by considerable practice of the technique of answering MCQs.

Dr Maclennan has produced a series of MCQs which cover in detail the Primary FRCA syllabus. The answer sections are clear and, where appropriate, supported by references to recent literature. Trainees commencing an anaesthesia training programme will find these MCQs useful to assess the depth of knowledge of the basic sciences which will be required of them, and those for whom the examination is imminent will find this series of books an invaluable means of self assessment and an indication of aspects of their knowledge and understanding which may need further work.

Dr D. Nolan, Regional Advisor for the North West

# INTRODUCTION

Having taken both anaesthetic and medicine postgraduate examinations, I think that it is always difficult to know how best to start revising. It is important to avoid that unpleasant drowning sensation when you look at all the information that you have to absorb! I personally find that sitting and reading a textbook is time consuming, not particularly memorable and not especially useful for actually passing the exam. The best way to find out the gaps in your knowledge is to do as many practice MCQs as you can. This will stimulate you to read around the topics you are less familiar with, whilst improving your exam technique.

These books are different from others on the market as they are subject based. Many candidates feel that they have a particular area of weakness. These books will at worst highlight those weaknesses and at best, allow you to home in on specific topics, making them your areas of strength.

Each book contains 150 MCQs, covering pharmacology and clinical in book 1, physics, clinical measurement, equipment and statistics in book 2, physiology and anatomy in book 3. Within each book, the questions are mostly based in subject groups. This enables you to revise a particular topic or, you can always take a selection of questions from each book to make a practice exam paper.

The questions are based on the primary syllabus but will also be useful for candidates studying for the basic science part of the final examination.

Being pocket sized, there is now no excuse! Carry one in the pocket of your theatre blues and do a few questions before the patient arrives in the anaesthetic room or even over lunch!

The examination period is a stressful time, so make best use of *all* the time that you have.

Good luck!

Kirsty

# Physiology

# MCQs

*Indicate your answers with a tick or cross in the boxes provided.*

### 3.1 Regarding the adult lungs:

☐ A  Movement of oxygen into the blood obeys Fick's law

☐ B  The blood : gas barrier has a surface area of more than $150 \text{ m}^2$

☐ C  There are approximately 10 million alveoli in total

☐ D  The main bronchi initially divide into segmental bronchi

☐ E  Respiratory bronchioles divide into terminal bronchioles

### 3.2 Regarding airway physiology:

☐ A  Through large airways air movement is secondary to bulk flow

☐ B  The main mechanism of ventilation of airways beyond the terminal bronchioles is by bulk flow

☐ C  Dust particles settle beyond the terminal bronchioles

☐ D  Nasal breathing increases the resistance by 50% compared with mouth breathing

☐ E  Bronchioles constitute the major resistance in the respiratory tree

## 3.1   Answers:

- A  True
- B  False
- C  False
- D  False
- E  False

Fick's law of diffusion states that the rate of diffusion across a membrane is proportional to the concentration gradient.

The blood : gas barrier has a surface area of 50–100 m².

The lungs contain approximately 300 million alveoli.

The divisions of the airways are as follows: the trachea divides to form the main bronchi, which form lobar bronchi, which form segmental bronchi; these lead to the terminal bronchioles, which are the smallest airways without alveoli; the terminal bronchioles then divide into respiratory bronchioles; these finally become the alveoli ducts, which are completely lined with alveoli. This area of the lung containing the alveoli is called the respiratory zone.

## 3.2   Answers:

- A  True
- B  False
- C  False
- D  True
- E  False

Beyond the terminal bronchioles gas movement is dependent upon diffusion not bulk flow as with the large airways.

Dust particles settle in the terminal bronchioles because the velocity of gas falls rapidly in this region.

Most airway resistance is secondary to proximal structures.

Bronchioles constitute only 10–20% of airway resistance.

## 3.3 Regarding the pulmonary circulation:

□ A Capillaries have a diameter of approximately 10 μm around the alveoli

□ B The normal value for systolic pulmonary artery pressure is approximately 25 mmHg

□ C Pressure in the right atrium is greater than that in the left atrium

□ D The pulmonary artery vessel wall comprises mostly smooth muscle

□ E Most pressure drop in the pulmonary circulation occurs just upstream of the capillary bed

## 3.3    Answers:

- A  True
- B  True
- C  False
- D  False
- E  False

Systolic pulmonary artery pressures are usually one-fifth of the systemic circulatory pressure. A normal range of 15–30 mmHg systolic and 0–8 mmHg diastolic is normally accepted. The pressure in the right atrium is about 2 mmHg compared with that of the left atrium, which is approximately 5 mmHg.

The pulmonary artery is very thin compared with the aorta secondary to its relative lack of smooth muscle, as it is such a low-pressure system in comparison.

Most pressure drop occurs within the capillary bed as compared with the systemic circulation where most pressure drop occurs just upstream of the capillary bed.

### 3.4 Lung volumes:

☐ A  Inspiratory reserve volume (IRV) is greater than expiratory reserve volumes (ERV)

☐ B  Residual volume (RV) is approximately 1–1.5 litres in a 20-year-old person

☐ C  Vital capacity (VC) decreases with age

☐ D  IRV, VC and tidal volume (TV) can all be measured with spirometry

☐ E  All measurements are recorded at standard temperature, pressure dry

**3.4    Answers:**

- A  True
- B  True
- C  True
- D  True
- E  False

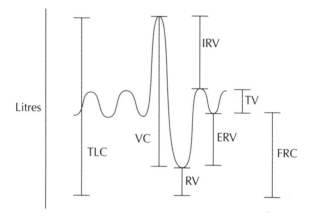

where TLC = total lung capacity
VC = vital capacity
RV = residual volume
IRV = inspiratory reserve volume
TV = tidal volume
ERV = expiratory reserve volume
FRC = functional residual capacity

Figure:   Lung volumes

IRV is approximately 3 litres compared with ERV, which is
approximately 1.5 litres. IRV increases with age to approximately
3 litres. VC therefore decreases with age. Only FRC, RV and TLC
cannot be measured with spirometry. All measurements are at
body temperature and pressure saturated.

## 3.5 Regarding ventilation:

☐ A An increase in alveolar ventilation always increases dead space ventilation

☐ B It is true to say: $V_A = V_{CO_2} \div P_{CO_2} \times K$ where $P_{CO_2}$ = partial pressure of carbon dioxide; $V_{CO_2}$ is volume exhaled of carbon dioxide per unit time; $K$ = a constant; $V_A$ = alveolar ventilation per unit time

☐ C Fowler's method of anatomical dead space analysis is calculated by plotting nitrogen concentration versus expired volume

☐ D The Bohr equation exactly states $V_D \div V_T = P_{a}CO_2 - P_{e}CO_2 \div P_{a}CO_2$

☐ E Physiological dead space is a measure of the entire lung not eliminating $CO_2$

### 3.5    Answers:

- A  False
- B  True
- C  True
- D  False
- E  True

Increasing alveolar ventilation by taking a deeper breath does not increase dead space, whereas increasing respiratory rate will.

Fowler's method of rapid nitrogen concentration analysis is plotted on a chart of nitrogen concentration on the $y$ axis and volume on the $x$ axis.

The Bohr equation is an equation of physiological dead space where:

$$V_D/V_T = (P_ACO_2 - P_eCO_2) \div P_aCO_2$$

ie $P_ACO_2$ or alveolar partial pressure of carbon dioxide. However, we commonly write $P_aCO_2$ as it is assumed that arterial $CO_2$ will be the same as alveolar.

**3.6    Regarding ventilation and diffusion within the lung:**

☐  A  In a lateral position the dependent lung will ventilate best

☐  B  The increase in partial pressure of nitrous oxide in the blood is perfusion limited

☐  C  The increase in partial pressure of carbon monoxide in the blood is perfusion limited

☐  D  In fibrotic lung conditions oxygen is perfusion limited

☐  E  With severe exercise oxygen may be diffusion limited

### 3.6    Answers:

- A  True
- B  True
- C  False
- D  False
- E  True

As with all positions, the lung tissue in the dependent portion ventilates best.

Diffusion is related to, among other things, the partial pressure difference of the gas.

There is almost no increase in the partial pressure of carbon monoxide in blood as it diffuses across and therefore it does not depend upon the amount of blood available. It is therefore said to be diffusion limited.

Nitrous oxide diffuses across but a partial pressure builds up in the blood and therefore the gradient is lost. This slows transfer and therefore it is said to be perfusion limited.

Oxygen can be diffusion limited with severe exercise especially when at altitude. With a reduction in $P_{AO_2}$ there is a decrease in alveolar/arterial gradient, which means that it diffuses more slowly into the fast moving circulation.

## 3.7    Regarding transfer factor for carbon monoxide:

☐ A   It is calculated based on the assumption that capillary carbon monoxide tension is zero

☐ B   $T_{LCO}$ (carbon monoxide transfer in the lung) differs from $D_{LCO}$ (carbon monoxide diffusion within the lung) in that it takes into account the chemical combination of carbon monoxide with haemoglobin as a rate-limiting step

☐ C   It is measured using a mixture of carbon monoxide and an insoluble gas

☐ D   The coefficient of gas transfer ($K_{CO}$) is the $T_{LCO}$ divided by $V_A$, where $T_{LCO}$ is carbon monoxide transfer in the lung and $V_A$ is alveolar volume

☐ E   $T_{LCO}$ is measured in mmol/min per kPa

## 3.8    Regarding transfer factor for carbon monoxide:

☐ A   Haemoglobin concentration does not significantly affect $T_{LCO}$ readings

☐ B   $T_{LCO}$ is a combination of alveolar volume × efficiency ($K_{CO}$) specific gas transfer

☐ C   $T_{LCO}$ is typically measured with an $F_{IO_2}$ of 0.5

☐ D   Pulmonary hypertension is associated with decrease $K_{CO}$ and decrease $V_A$

☐ E   Asthma is associated with a decreased $T_{LCO}$

### 3.7 Answers:

- A True
- B True
- C True
- D True
- E True

Other countries still measure $D_LCO$ (ml/min per mmHg). The change in concentration of the insoluble gas enables the calculation of the alveolar volume.

Gas exchange capacity ($T_LCO$) = alveolar volume ($V_A$) × efficiency ($K_CO$). A reduction in $T_LCO$ can occur secondary to a decrease in $V_A$ or decrease in $K_CO$ or a combination of both.

### 3.8 Answers:

- A False
- B True
- C False
- D False
- E False

Haemoglobin concentration will significantly influence the $T_LCO$ as the chemical binding of carbon monoxide to haemoglobin is a rate-limiting step and therefore all readings are corrected to reference haemoglobin of 14.5 g/dl with a standard equation (1 g reduction in haemoglobin leads to a 4% fall in $T_LCO$.

$K_CO$ is measured with a mix of carbon monoxide/insoluble gas and typically 18% oxygen, as oxygen competes with carbon monoxide for haemoglobin-binding sites.

Pulmonary hypertension is associated with a decrease in $K_CO$ but a normal $V_A$ as is pulmonary embolism.

$T_LCO$ may be slightly elevated in asthma and is markedly elevated in pulmonary haemorrhage secondary to the extravascular haemoglobin that binds carbon monoxide.

**3.9    The following are true of pulmonary physiology:**

☐  A  The pulmonary arteries accompany the bronchi as far as the terminal bronchioles before becoming capillary bed

☐  B  Two large veins drain blood from lungs to the left atrium

☐  C  <u>Mean</u> pulmonary artery pressure is approximately 20–30 mmHg

☐  D  As the lung volume increases the extra-alveolar arteries and veins increase in size

☐  E  A rise in pulmonary artery pressure causes a rise in pulmonary vascular resistance in the normal lung

**3.10   Pulmonary blood flow:**

☐  A  Can be measured using indicator dilution techniques

☐  B  Can be calculated with knowledge of oxygen consumption alone

☐  C  Is lower in west zone 3 than in west zone 1

☐  D  Reduction by smooth muscle contraction in small arterioles accounts for decrease blood flow in hypoxic areas

☐  E  Reduction by hypoxic pulmonary vasoconstriction is chiefly a result of decreased partial pressure of oxygen in alveoli

**3.9    Answers:**
- A  True
- B  False
- C  False
- D  True
- E  False

Four large veins drain blood from the lung to the left atrium.
Mean pulmonary artery pressures are within a range between
10 and 15 mmHg.
As the lung expands the extra-alveolar vessels are subjected to the
expanding pull of the parenchyma and therefore increase in size.
As the pulmonary artery pressure rises pulmonary vascular
resistance falls within normal lungs secondary to distension and
recruitment of capillaries.

**3.10    Answers:**
- A  True
- B  False
- C  False
- D  True
- E  True

Pulmonary blood flow can be measured with haemodilution
techniques or calculated using Fick's principle. Application of
Fick's principle denotes that oxygen consumption per minute is
equal to the amount of oxygen taken up by the lung per minute.
To calculate pulmonary blood flow from this principle, oxygen
consumption, arterial oxygen and mixed venous oxygen
concentrations are needed. The equation reads:

$Q = V_{O_2} \div (CaO_2 - C\bar{v}O_2)$

where $Q$ is pulmonary blood flow, $V_{O_2}$ = oxygen consumption
per minute and $CaO_2$ and $C\bar{v}O_2$ are arterial and mixed venous
oxygen concentrations respectively.
West zone 3 has a blood flow unaffected by alveolar pressure as
arterial pressure is greater than venous pressure, which is greater
than alveolar pressure, whereas west zone 1 alveolar pressure is
greater than arterial, so alveolar pressure greatly affects arterial
blood flow.

**3.11    Pulmonary vascular resistance (PVR) is increased by:**

☐  A   A decrease in cardiac output

☐  B   Nitric oxide

☐  C   Sympathetic nervous system

☐  D   Acidosis

☐  E   Hypothermia

**3.12    Regarding haemoglobin:**

☐  A   Each haem binds one $Fe^{2+}$

☐  B   Each haemoglobin molecule carries one oxygen molecule

☐  C   Methaemoglobin formation is secondary to oxidation of $Fe^{2+}$ to $Fe^{3+}$

☐  D   2,3-Diphosphoglycerate (2,3-DPG) binds the α chains of haemoglobin

☐  E   The presence of methaemoglobin will increase the Hüfner constant

**3.11    Answers:**

- A  True
- B  False
- C  True
- D  True
- E  True

$$PVR = (PAP - LAP) \div CO$$

where PAP = pulmonary artery pressure, LAP = left atrial pressure and CO = cardiac output.

A good anaesthetic decreases PVR, ie a patient who is calm, anaesthetised, warm, well oxygenated, normocapnic and with normal pH.

**3.12    Answers:**

- A  True
- B  False
- C  True
- D  False
- E  False

Each haemoglobin binds one $Fe^{2+}$.

Four haem molecules form one haemoglobin, which can carry four oxygen molecules.

2,3-DPG binds to the β chains of deoxygenated haemoglobin, changing protein conformation and decreasing oxygen affinity, so shifting the oxygen dissociation curve to the right.

The Hüfner constant is the volume (measured in millilitres) of oxygen carried by 1 g haemoglobin. It is decreased if the level of non-oxygen-binding globin increases, eg with methaemoglobin.

**3.13    The oxyhaemoglobin dissociation curve is shifted to the right with:**

☐  A  An increase in temperature

☐  B  An increase in carbon monoxide

☐  C  An increase in 2,3-DPG

☐  D  Pregnancy

☐  E  Growth hormone

### 3.13   Answers:

- A  True
- B  False
- C  True
- D  True
- E  True

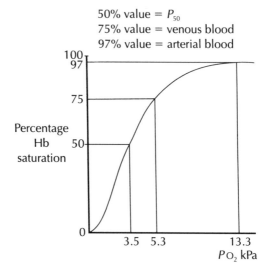

50% value = $P_{50}$
75% value = venous blood
97% value = arterial blood

Figure:   Oxyhaemoglobin dissociation curve

It helps to remember that an exercising muscle shifts the curve to the right. An exercising muscle will be hot, have high $CO_2$ and be acidotic.

A shift to the right will decrease the oxygen affinity of haemoglobin and therefore promotes unloading of oxygen in the tissues.

The curve is shifted to the left by methaemoglobinaemia, fetal haemoglobin and carbon monoxide poisoning.

### 3.14    Regarding gas carriage in blood:

- ☐  A  Carbon dioxide in venous blood is carried predominantly as $HCO_3^-$
- ☐  B  Carbon dioxide is twice as soluble in blood as oxygen
- ☐  C  The Haldane effect refers to the increased oxygen binding once one oxygen has bound to a haemoglobin molecule
- ☐  D  Anaemic patients will have reduced dissolved oxygen compared with patients with normal haemoglobin
- ☐  E  Oxygen has an affinity for haemoglobin approximately 240 times less than that of carbon monoxide

## 3.14   Answers:

- A  True
- B  False
- C  False
- D  False
- E  True

Carbon dioxide is approximately 20 times more soluble in blood when compared with oxygen.

The Haldane effect refers to the increased affinity of deoxygenated haemoglobin to carry carbon dioxide. This is because reduced haemoglobin is better able to bind hydrogen ions, so allowing for more transport of carbon dioxide as bicarbonate dissolved in the blood. In addition, the complex of hydrogen ion and reduced haemoglobin is then able to combine with carbon dioxide directly to form carbamino groups, which again increases its transport.

Anaemic patients will have a decreased overall oxygen carriage secondary to decreased haemoglobin; however, the dissolved oxygen will not be reduced.

Remember: oxygen carriage (ml $O_2$/100 ml blood) = (1.39 × Hb × saturation) + 0.003 $PaO_2$) in mmHg.

**3.15   Regarding chest wall movement:**

☐  A  Most of the work of breathing is to overcome the resistance in the airways

☐  B  The internal oblique muscles aid inspiration

☐  C  The external intercostal muscles pull the rib cage upwards and outwards

☐  D  The internal intercostal muscles aid inspiration

☐  E  During exercise the diaphragm can descend up to 10 cm

**3.16   Compliance of the lung:**

☐  A  In the normal human lung is 200 ml/cmH$_2$O

☐  B  Decreases in old age

☐  C  When specific compliance takes the lung size into account

☐  D  Decreases during an acute asthma attack

☐  E  Increases in patients with pulmonary oedema

### 3.15    Answers:

- A  False
- B  False
- C  True
- D  False
- E  True

Most of the work of breathing (approximately 65%) is to overcome the elastic work of the lungs. This is why expiration in quiet breathing is passive.

The internal oblique muscles have no role in inspiration but can assist forced expiration.

The internal intercostals aid forced expiration and move the rib cage inwards and downwards.

### 3.16    Answers:

- A  True
- B  False
- C  True
- D  False
- E  False

There are a number of causes of increased lung compliance including old age and emphysema, possibly due to the changes in elasticity of the lung.

Acute asthma increases compliance. The mechanism for this is not clear.

A decrease in compliance is seen with pulmonary fibrosis and oedema and with an increase in pulmonary venous pressure.

Specific compliance allows the comparison of compliance in different sized lungs.

### 3.17 Surfactant:

☐ A Is synthesised by type I alveolar epithelial cells

☐ B Has its main constituent, synthesised from amino acids in the lung

☐ C Helps to keep the alveoli dry

☐ D Production is affected by smoking

☐ E Production is partly under the control of the hypothalamic–pituitary–adrenal axis

### 3.18 Regarding airway resistance:

☒ A It predominantly occurs in the segmental bronchi

☒ B During turbulent flow, flow rate is proportional to pressure $\sqrt{P}$

☒ C The use of helium decreases turbulence as it decreases viscosity of the gas

☐ D It is calculated by the pressure difference between the alveoli and the mouth divided by a flow rate

☒ E During quiet respiration the oxygen cost of breathing is approximately 30%

### 3.17    Answers:

- A  False
- B  False
- C  True
- D  True
- E  True

Surfactant is synthesised by type II alveolar epithelial cells.

The main constituent is dipalmitoyl phosphatidylcholine, which is synthesised from fatty acids in the lung. It is thought to have its effect secondary to the strong repulsion of neighbouring hydrophilic parts that push each other away and so splint the alveoli open (most noticeably when at low volumes).

Production is reduced in areas of poor perfusion and in heavy smokers. The cells responsible for the production of surfactant begin to appear at 24 weeks of fetal gestation.

### 3.18    Answers:

- A  False
- B  False
- C  False
- D  True
- E  False

Most airway resistance is encountered at the terminal bronchi with less than 20% of resistance occurring beyond airways of less than 2 mm in diameter.

During turbulent flow, flow rate is proportional to the square root of the pressure.

Helium decreases the density not the viscosity of gas mixtures. Remember that during turbulent flow decreasing the density is important compared with decreasing the viscosity in laminar flow.

The oxygen cost of breathing during quiet respiration is 5–10% but during exertion this can increase to 30%.

**3.19   The following are true of the central control of breathing:**

☑ A   Dorsal medullary cells are thought to be involved in triggering respiration

☑ B   Nerves terminating in the tractus solitarius affect inspiratory cells

☐ C   The upper pons is thought to regulate inspiratory volume

☑ D   The apneustic centre is situated in the lower pons

☐ E   The expiratory cells of the medulla are inactive during quiet respiration

**3.20   Regarding chemoreceptors and their function:**

☑ A   Central chemoreceptors are situated within the medulla

☑ B   Dissolved carbon dioxide in the cerebrospinal fluid (CSF) acts directly on the central chemoreceptors to bring about a change in ventilation

☑ C   Acidosis is compensated for more quickly in the arterial circulation when compared with the CSF

☑ D   Carotid body chemoreceptors respond to $CO_2$ $O_2$ and pH changes

☐ E   Aortic body chemoreceptors respond to changes in pH

**3.19   Answers:**

- A   True    (D)VE (dorsal insp, ventral exp)
- B   True
- C   True    tractus    {vagus
- D   True    solitarius {glossoph.
- E   True

Dorsal medullary cells are thought to be mainly associated with inspiration.

Ventral medullary cells are thought to control expiration and are only active during forced expiration.

The upper pons houses the pneumotaxic centre, which is thought to inhibit inspiration and therefore control tidal volume and respiratory rate. The lower pons houses the apneustic centre, which in animal studies increase the inspiratory period.

Vagus and glossopharyngeal nerves terminate in the tractus solitarius and affect the inspiratory dorsal medullary cells.

**3.20   Answers:**

- A   False
- B   False
- C   False
- D   True
- E   False

Central chemoreceptors are outside the respiratory centre, below the ventral surface of the medulla. They respond directly to changes in hydrogen ions because of carbon dioxide dissociation.

A change in pH in the CSF is quickly compensated for with $HCO_3^-$ transport across the blood–brain barrier. This occurs more quickly than the process of renal compensation for arterial acidosis.

Carotid body chemoreceptors respond to pH, $O_2$ and $CO_2$. Aortic body chemoreceptors respond to changes in $O_2$ and $CO_2$ but not to changes in pH.

**3.21 When studying the control of ventilation:**

☑ A The Hering–Breuer reflex is activated by a large inspiratory volume of greater than 1 litre

☒ B J-receptor stimulation leads to deep inspiration

☑ C Carbon dioxide levels are the main factor in the control of ventilation

☑ D The ventilatory response to carbon dioxide is decreased if the work of breathing is increased

☑ E In the absence of peripheral chemoreceptors, hypoxaemia depresses ventilation

**3.22 Regarding the respiratory system during exercise:**

☒ A Oxygen consumption increases exponentially

☒ B Respiratory quotient or respiratory exchange ratio decreases

☑ C There is an increase in the diffusing capacity of the lung

☒ D Ventilation and cardiac output increase by similar values

☒ E There is a large difference between inspired and expired oxygen concentrations (when compared with non-exercising values)

### 3.21 Answers:

- A True
- B False
- C True
- D True
- E True

The Hering–Breuer reflex causes an increase in expiratory time triggered by a large inspiratory volume that is detected by pulmonary stretch receptors.

J (or juxtacapillary) receptors are thought to be found in the alveolar walls. They respond to pulmonary capillary engorgement and interstitial oedema and cause shallow rapid breathing (via non-myelinated vagal fibres).

Hypoxaemia is detected only by peripheral chemoreceptors and, without them, the respiratory centre is actually depressed by a decrease in oxygen.

### 3.22 Answers:

- A False
- B False
- C True
- D False
- E False

Oxygen consumption increases lineally until reaching a plateau at the $O_2$ max.

Respiratory quotient (normally quoted as 0.8) increases as carbohydrate becomes the main energy source rather than fat.

Diffusing capacity of the lungs increases as there is increased alveolar capillary interface secondary to recruitment of capillaries.

Ventilation increases approximately four times that of cardiac output.

The difference between exercising and non-exercising inspired and expired oxygen values is minimal.

Reference: Physiological effects of exercise. *Continuing Education in Anaesthesia, Critical Care and Pain* 2004; 4(6): 185–8.

## 3.23  Regarding respiration at altitude:

☑ A  Once the barometric pressure is below 6.3 kPa the inspired oxygen concentration is zero

☐ B  The key to altitude survival is hyperventilation

☑ C  Hyperventilation increases linearly during the first 7 days at altitude

☐ D  Erythropoietin production means that the oxygen-carrying capacity of blood can be above normal

☐ E  At very high altitudes, breathing is aided by decreased density of gas

## 3.24  Regarding the respiratory effects of diving:

☒ A  Pressure increases by 1 atmosphere per 100 metres

☐ B  Risk of 'the bends' increases with increasing depth of dive

☐ C  Helium : oxygen mix can be used to decrease the incidence of nitrogen narcosis when diving

☐ D  Oxygen toxicity can lead to convulsions

☐ E  Hydrogen can be used as a gas mix with oxygen for deep dives

**3.23   Answers:**

- A  True
- B  True
- C  False
- D  True
- E  True

The initial acclimatisation response to high altitude is hyperventilation. This is driven by the hypoxic stimulation of peripheral chemoreceptors.

Hyperventilation continues until halted by a decrease in carbon dioxide and respiratory alkalosis (before 7 days), which is detected by the central and peripheral chemoreceptors. The CSF pH is corrected first then the arterial pH is corrected after approximately 2–3 days. Once corrected, hyperventilation continues. With time, carotid body sensitivity to hypoxia decreases.

**3.24   Answers:**

- A  False
- B  True
- C  True
- D  True
- E  True

Pressure increases by 1 atm per 10 m. The risk of developing 'the bends' or nitrogen narcosis is greater with longer, deeper dives as this increases the partial pressure of nitrogen and therefore forces the insoluble gas into tissues.

Helium–oxygen mix can be used for deep dives as it decreases the risk of nitrogen narcosis and also decreases the density, so decreases the work of breathing.

Oxygen toxicity can be preceded by ringing in the ears and facial twitching and can occur at partial pressures of oxygen exceeding 1 atm.

**3.25 Hypoxic pulmonary vasoconstriction (HPV) is inhibited by:**

- ☒ A Hypercapnia ↓
- ☒ B High left atrial pressure
- ☒ C Vasoconstrictors
- ☒ D Lung handling at surgery
- ☐ E High pulmonary arterial $P_{O_2}$

**3.25    Answers:**

- A  False
- B  True
- C  False
- D  True
- E  False

HPV occurs when the smooth muscle around arterioles contracts, so reducing blood supply to the alveolar. How it occurs is unknown but deinnervated lung is able to produce the effect and so it is presumed not to be under central control.

It is mainly driven by a decrease in alveolar $PO_2$ (not arterial).

Hypocapnia inhibits hypoxic pulmonary vasoconstriction.

Vasodilators inhibit hypoxic pulmonary vasoconstriction.

### 3.26 Regarding calcium:

☒ A Approximately 70% of total calcium in blood is protein bound

☐ B Acidosis increases ionised calcium concentration

☐ C For every gram per litre albumin < 40 g/l in blood, 0.02 mmol/l must be added to obtain a true total plasma calcium value

☒ D Hypercalcaemia causes a prolongation of the QT interval on an ECG

☒ E The main site of calcium regulation in the kidney is in the proximal tubule

**3.26    Answers:**

- A  False
- B  True
- C  True
- D  False
- E  False

Approximately 50% of total plasma calcium exists in the biologically active ionised form, with the non-diffusible calcium bound to albumin (predominantly) and globin. A total of 99% of total body calcium is in bone.

Acidosis increases ionised calcium. Hyperventilation causes alkalosis with a decrease in ionised calcium, which presents as tetany, carpopedal spasm or laryngeal stridor.

For each 0.1 decrease in pH, ionised calcium rises by approximately 0.05 mmol/l.

Passive absorption of calcium occurs predominantly in the ileum. Active absorption, which is dependent on vitamin D occurs in the duodenum, jejunum and large intestine.

A total of 85% of renally filtered calcium is reabsorbed, 60% in the proximal tubule. However, it is the distal tubule that controls actual calcium levels under the influence of parathyroid hormone.

Hypocalcaemia prolongs the QT interval. Hypercalcaemia shortens it.

Reference: Thyroid and parathyroid hormones and calcium homeostasis. *Anaesthesia and Intensive Care Medicine* 2005; 6: 333–6.

**3.27  Regarding thyroid metabolism:**

A  Thyroid-stimulating hormone (TSH) increases the uptake of iodide from the gut    I⁻ OIL RIG.

B  The initial reaction of iodide within the thyroid is that of reduction to form iodine

C  Iodine does not bind to thyroglobulin within the thyroid

D  Iodinase enzymes are needed to catalyse the reaction of iodine with tyrosine

E  Peroxidases catalyse the condensation reaction of two diiodotyrosine molecules to form thyroxine ($T_4$)

**3.28  The following statements regarding thyroid hormones are correct:**

A  TRH (thyroid-releasing hormone) is a tripeptide secreted by the hypothalamus

B  TRH acts via cAMP

C  TSH acts via cAMP.

D  $T_4$ acts via cAMP

E  Triiodolthyronine ($T_3$) and $T_4$ inhibit the release of TRH

## 3.27 Answers:

- A  True
- B  False
- C  False
- D  True
- E  True

TSH increases iodide ($I^-$) absorption from the gut. Iodide is actively taken up into the thyroid follicular cells where it is oxidised to form iodine. A process catalysed by peroxidase on the apical membrane of the follicular cells (hydrogen peroxide accepts the electron).

Once formed, iodine then binds to tyrosine in thyroglobulin to form monoiodotyrosine and then diiodotyrosine.

Condensation of two di-iodotyrosine forms $T_4$. Condensation of monoiodotyrosine and diiodotyrosine yields $T_3$.

Reference: Thyroid and parathyroid hormones and calcium homeostasis. *Anaesthesia and Intensive Care Medicine* 2005; 6: 333–6.

## 3.28 Answers:

- A  True
- B  False
- C  True
- D  False
- E  True

TRH acts via phospholipase C resulting in increased calcium release from endoplasmic reticulum and activation of protein kinase C. This causes the release of TSH from the pituitary.

TSH acts via cAMP stimulating protein kinase A.

$T_4$ is initially the deiodinated to $T_3$, which then binds to intracellular receptors. This initiates nuclear gene transcription so increasing messenger RNA, which activates cytoplasmic ribosomes and increases cellular protein synthesis.

**3.29  Essential amino acids obtained from the diet include:**

A  Tyrosine

B  Methionine

C  Leucine

D  Glutamine

E  Aminobutyric acid

**3.30  Hepatic physiology:**

A  The portal triad contains the hepatic vein

B  The periportal hepatocytes receive the most oxygenated blood supply

C  The centrilobular hepatocytes are the main site of drug biotransformation

D  Hepatocytes outnumber Kupffer cells

E  In an adult, Kupffer cells have haematopoetic function

**3.29   Answers:**

- A  True
- B  True
- C  True
- D  False
- E  False

Essential amino acids obtained from diet include valine, isoleucine, methionine, phenylalanine, tyrosine, lysine, leucine and threonine. These are all essential for life.

Arginine and histidine are essential for growth not life.

A very simple pneumonic may help you remember:

*Very important little things.*

**V** from very

**IMPT** in important

**LL** in little

**T** in things.

Reference: Power I, Kam P. *Principles of Physiology for the Anaesthetist.*, p. 318, Hodder Arnold, 2001.

**3.30   Answers:**

- A  False
- B  True
- C  True
- D  True
- E  False

The portal triad consists of the portal vein, hepatic artery and bile duct.

The periportal zone surrounds the hepatic arteriole and is highest in oxygen content and has the highest metabolic rate. This zone is mostly involved with protein synthesis.

Kupffer cells are macrophages. They only have significant haematopoetic function in the fetus.

**3.31** **Regarding carbohydrate metabolism:**

☒ A  Healthy adult livers contain approximately 1 kg glycogen

☐ B  Gluconeogenesis in the liver is facilitated by insulin

☐ C  Insulin secretion is stimulated by a decreased portal blood sugar

☒ D  Thirty-eight ATP molecules are produced by the aerobic metabolism of glucose

☐ E  Glycogen formation in the liver is under the control of two enzymes: glycogen synthetase and glycogen phosphorylase

**3.32** **Regarding lipid metabolism:**

☒ A  50% of triglycerides from diet are hydrolysed to glycerol and fatty acids

☐ B  Short-chain fatty acids are transported directly to the liver by the portal vein

☐ C  Chylomicrons consist of long-chain fatty acids that have been re-esterified and covered in phospholipids and protein layer

☒ D  Free fatty acids are produced by the effect of lipoprotein lipase on chylomicrons

☐ E  Acetyl-CoA is formed by the metabolism of free fatty acids

**3.31    Answers:**

- A  False
- B  False
- C  False
- D  True
- E  True

Healthy liver contains approximately 100 g glycogen.

Two ATP molecules are yielded from the breakdown of glucose to pyruvate and a further 36 ATP molecules are produced from the breakdown of pyruvate in the tricarboxylic acid cycle.

Gluconeogenesis is facilitated by glucagon, which increases alanine transport into the hepatocytes and pyruvate into the mitochondria.

Insulin secretion is stimulated by high portal blood sugar. It causes inhibition of glycogenolysis and gluconeogenesis but stimulates pyruvate dehydrogenase and glucose phosphorylation to form glycogen.

**3.32    Answers:**

- A  True
- B  True
- C  True
- D  True
- E  True

Approximately 40–50% of dietary triglycerides are partially hydrolysed to monoglycerides.

Long-chain fatty acids are over 12 carbon atoms long. They are re-esterified after absorption, then covered with phospholipids and a protein layer to form chylomicrons.

Lipoprotein lipase hydrolyses the chylomicrons to produce free fatty acids.

The continued oxidation of acetyl-CoA yields ketone bodies.

### 3.33  Regarding the physiology of bile:

- ☑ A  Approximately the same amounts of bile and saliva are produced per day
- ☒ B  Bile salts are made in the liver from fatty acids
- ☑ C  Unconjugated bilirubin is water soluble
- ☑ D  Urobilinogen is formed from unconjugated bilirubin
- ☑ E  Stercobilinogen is formed in the liver

### 3.34  Protein metabolism:

- ☑ A  Serum albumin has a half-life of 10 days
- ☑ B  Raised plasma glucagon levels stimulate the catabolism of amino acids in the liver
- ☒ C  ATP molecules are produced when $CO_2$ and ammonia enter the urea cycle
- ☒ D  The urea cycle occurs in liver and muscles
- ☑ E  Deaminated alanine can enter the gluconeogenic pathway as pyruvate

**3.33    Answers:**

- A  True
- B  False
- C  False
- D  False
- E  False

Approximately I litre of bile is produced per day.

Bile acids are produced from cholesterol in the liver. Once these bile acids have been acted on in the gut they form secondary bile acids. When conjugated with taurine or glycine, bile salts are formed.

Haemoglobin is converted first to biliverdin then to bilirubin, which is bound to albumin and transported to the liver. In the liver it is conjugated with glucuronides (now it is water soluble.) It is excreted in bile.

Gut bacteria cause the formation of stercobilinogen (passed out in stool) and urobilinogen, which passes into the portal circulation and is excreted in the urine.

**3.34    Answers:**

- A  False
- B  True
- C  False
- D  False
- E  True

Serum albumin has a half-life of 20 days.

Breakdown of amino acids is via oxidative deamination. Initially amino groups are removed and eventually form glutamate and aspartate. Glutamate forms ammonia under the influence of glutamate dehydrogenase.

Aspartate, ammonia and $CO_2$ (+ 2 ATP molecules) enter the urea cycle to form urea. The urea cycle cannot take place in muscle, so the transaminated amino acids pass to the liver in the form of alanine. Deaminated alanine is pyruvate, which can therefore enter the gluconeogenic pathway to become glucose.

**3.35  Regarding the systemic circulation:**

    A  At rest two-thirds of the capillaries are patent

    B  The velocity of blood through veins is greater than through the capillaries

    C  In a supine patient blood is divided equally between systemic and pulmonary circulations

    D  The Windkessel effect refers to the prevention of retrograde flow by the venous circulation

    E  Resting cardiac output is approximately 5–6 l/min

**3.36  The following are correct approximate values for blood flow to organs:**

    A  The brain receives 500 ml/min

    B  The coronary circulation receives 250 ml/min

    C  The kidneys receive 750 ml/min (total)

    D  Skeletal muscle at rest receives 250 ml/min

    E  Abdominal organs receive 1 l/min

**3.35    Answers:**

- A  False
- B  True
- C  False
- D  False
- E  True

At rest only a quarter of the systemic capillaries are patent.

Relative velocities are as follows:

- aorta 20 cm/s.
- capillaries 0.5 mm/s.
- vena cava 12 cm/s.

In a supine patient 75% of blood volume is in the systemic circulation compared with 16% in the pulmonary circulation and 8% in the heart.

The Windkessel effect refers to the conversion of the intermittent ventricular output of blood into a continuous pulsatile arterial flow. It results from the stored potential energy in the elastic walls of the aorta.

**3.36    Answers:**

- A  False
- B  True
- C  False
- D  False
- E  False

| Organ | Approximate blood flow (ml/min) |
|---|---|
| Brain | 750 |
| Coronary circulation | 250 |
| Kidneys | 1100 |
| Abdominal organs | 1400 |
| Skin | 500 |
| Skeletal muscle (at rest) | 1200 |
| Skeletal muscle (active) | 20 000 |

### 3.37 Cardiac muscle fibres:

- ☐ A Between right and left atria are continuous
- ☐ B Have no striations
- ☐ C Form a true syncytium
- ☐ D Are shorter and thicker than skeletal muscle fibres
- ☐ E Form networks with intercalated discs between fibres containing gap junctions

### 3.38 Regarding myocardial tissue physiology:

- ☐ A Myocardial oxygen consumption is 8–10 ml/min per 100 g tissue
- ☐ B Myocardial oxygen consumption is greater than brain oxygen consumption
- ☐ C Approximate coronary venous blood oxygen content is 5 ml/100 ml blood
- ☐ D Carbohydrate and lactate make up the main energy substrate of the heart
- ☐ E Oxygen extraction by cardiac muscle increases significantly during exercise

**3.37    Answers:**

- A  True
- B  False
- C  False
- D  True
- E  True

Continuous muscle fibres between the right and left atria enable them to contract simultaneously. (There are also continuous muscle fibres between the right and left ventricles.)

Cardiac muscle is striated similar to skeletal muscle but it does not form a true syncytium as each myocardial cell has its own nucleus within its own membrane (rather than a mass of protoplasm with many nuclei forming one cell).

However, due to the connections between adjacent cells, cardiac muscle acts as a functional syncytium.

**3.38    Answers:**

- A  True
- B  True
- C  True
- D  False
- E  False

Brain uses 3–5 ml $O_2$/min  per 100 g tissue.

The predominant cardiac substrate of metabolism is esterified and non-esterified fatty acids at 60% compared with carbohydrate at 40%.

Myocardial oxygen extraction at rest is almost 60%, the only practical way to increase oxygen delivery to the heart is to increase the blood flow.

**3.39    Regarding ventricular muscle action potentials:**

☒ A   Phase 0 is the result of calcium channel opening
☒ B   Phase 1 is the result of calcium channel opening
☒ C   Phase 4 has a resting potential of −70 mV
☒ D   Phase 2 is the plateau phase
☒ E   Phase 3 sees a return to normal permeability of potassium, calcium and sodium

**3.39    Answers:**

- A  False
- B  False
- C  False
- D  True
- E  True

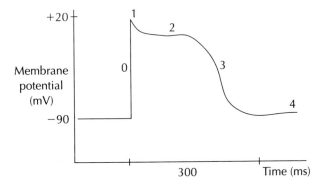

Figure:    Cardiac action potential

Resting membrane potential is −90 mV during phase 4 secondary to potassium permeability.

Phase 0 sees an increase in permeability to sodium as fast sodium channels open. Potassium conductance decreases.

Phase 1 is partial repolarisation as sodium permeability decreases.

Phase 2 is the plateau as calcium permeability rises on the background of a decrease in sodium permeability.

Phase 3 sees a return to normal permeability as in option E.

**3.40   Action potential of the SA/AV node:**

☑ A  Phase 0 sodium enters the cell

☑ B  Phase 4 calcium enters via L-type channels

☑ C  Phase 3 potassium flows out of the cell

☑ D  Parasympathetic nervous supply increases potassium
permeability  Hyperpolarisation.

☐ E  The rate of depolarisation in phase 4 is slower in the
atrioventricular (AV) compared with the sinoatrial (SA) node

**3.40    Answers:**

- A  False
- B  False
- C  True
- D  True
- E  True

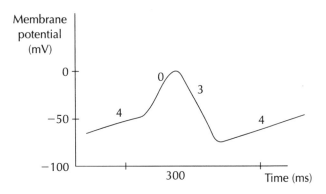

Figure:    Sinoatrial node action potential

Phase 4 is secondary to a decrease in potassium permeability and an increase in calcium influx via T-type channels.

The threshold potential is reached at −50 mV, leading to phase 0 depolarisation via L-type calcium channels.

Phase 3 is repolarisation and is secondary to potassium efflux.

Parasympathetic innovation increases potassium permeability, inhibiting cardiac activity. Sympathetic innovation increases calcium channel opening.

**3.41    Cardiovascular physiology:**

- ☑ A  The absolute refractory period of myocardial fibres is 250 ms
- ☒ B  Catecholamine action on the heart is mediated by Gq-coupled phospholipase C
- ☑ C  Digoxin increases intracellular sodium
- ☑ D  The natural SA node discharge rate is 100 beats/min
- ☒ E  Bachmann's bundle is within the bundle of His

**3.42    With reference to the ECG:**

- ☒ A  The normal QT interval is 0.45–0.55 s
- ☒ B  Lead 1 records between the right arm and left leg
- ☑ C  The normal second heart sound is heard at the beginning of the R wave
- ☑ D  Isovolumetric contraction coincides with the R wave
- ☑ E  Aortic pressure is at its highest immediately before the T wave

**3.41 Answers:**

- A False
- B False
- C True
- D True
- E False

The absolute refractory period is 200 ms. The relative refractory period is 50 ms.

Catecholamines act via $\beta_1$-receptors, ie Gs-coupled adenylyl cyclase to increase calcium channel opening. They also phosphorylate myosin and phospholamban (responsible for calcium, reuptake) and so increase both contraction and relaxation.

Digoxin inhibits the $Na^+K^+$-ATPase pump, thereby increasing intracellular sodium and so indirectly increases intracellular calcium, leading to an increase in force of contraction.

Bachmann's bundle transmits the action potential from the SA to the left atrium. It then travels to the AV node via internodal pathways.

**3.42 Answers:**

- A False
- B False
- C False
- D True
- E True

A normal QT interval is 0.35–0.43 s.

Lead 1 records between the right arm and left arm.

Lead 2 records between the right arm and left leg.

Lead 3 records between the left arm and left leg. (This can be remembered by the number of Ls in the recording limbs, eg lead 3 has 3 Ls – left arm and left leg.)

The second heart sound is auscultated at the end of the T wave on an ECG.

**3.43    Regarding cardiac physiology:**

☐ A  Atrial contraction accounts for 40% of the end-diastolic ventricular volume

☐ B  Normal stroke volume is approximately 70 ml

☐ C  The aortic valve closes after the pulmonary valve

☐ D  An increased resting length of the papillary muscle increases the sensitivity of troponin to calcium

☐ E  Overstretched cardiac muscle produces a weak isometric contraction

**3.43    Answers:**

- A   False
- B   True
- C   False
- D   True
- E   True

Atrial contraction accounts for 15–20% of the end-diastolic volume.

The aortic valve closes before the pulmonary valve.

Option D is correct, it also increases the concentration of free calcium within the cell and therefore increases the force of contraction.

Overstretched fibres have a high resting tension but are unable to produce a forceful contraction.

**3.44    Regarding the ventricular pressure–volume curve relationship:**

☐  A  The pressure–volume loop for the right ventricle is almost triangular

☐  B  The area enclosed by the pressure–volume curve reflects the stroke work done by the left ventricle

☐  C  An increase in preload significantly increases the area enclosed by the pressure–volume curve of the left ventricle

☐  D  During ischaemia the pressure–volume loop appears to lean leftwards

☐  E  The gradient of the end-systolic pressure–volume line provides an index of contractility

**3.44** **Answers:**

- A True
- B True
- C True
- D False
- E True

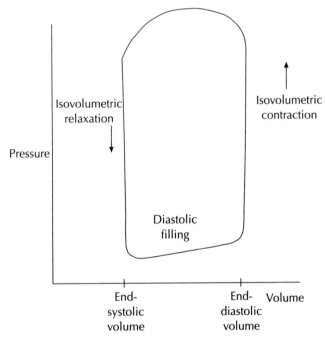

Figure: Left ventricular pressure–volume loop

During ischaemia the pressure–volume curve leans rightwards. This is as the fibres lengthen (rather than shorten) during isovolumetric contraction because they bulge outwards and the fibres shorten during isovolumetric relaxation. This shortening may be active or recoil, related to the critically ischaemic ventricle.

**3.45    Regarding the left ventricular pressure–volume loop
        interpretation:**

☐ A  Compliance is reflected by the slope of the diastolic pressure–
      volume curve

☐ B  Ejection fraction is a poor marker of systolic function

☐ C  The cardiac pump is very energy efficient

☐ D  The triangle enclosed by the end-systolic pressure–volume
      line, the end-diastolic pressure–volume line and the line
      representing isovolumetric relaxation represents the amount of
      potential energy available during contraction

☐ E  The pressure–volume area represents total mechanical work
      and heat generated

**3.46    Regarding the characteristics of blood and blood flow:**

☐ A  Blood is a newtonian fluid

☐ B  In small blood vessels, the red cells occupy the central fast-
      flowing stream rather than being adjacent to the lumen wall

☐ C  Plasma has a relative viscosity when compared with water
      of 0.9

☐ D  Capillaries create the greatest resistance to blood flow

☐ E  In small diameter vessels the apparent viscosity of blood
      reduces, so reducing the pressure required to perfuse the
      microcirculation

**3.45   Answers:**

- A   True
- B   False
- C   False
- D   True
- E   True

Compliance reflects volume change per unit change in pressure.

Ejection fraction = (end-diastolic volume [EDV] – end-systolic volume [ESV]) ÷ end-diastolic volume (EDV).

Ejection fraction is a good marker of systolic function.

The cardiac pump is not energy efficient: approximately 20% at best. Energy is lost as heat.

The pressure–volume area is a summation of the potential energy area and the external work area.

**3.46   Answers:**

- A   False
- B   True
- C   False
- D   False
- E   True

Newtonian fluid is a homogeneous fluid with a viscosity unaffected by its flow rate. Blood is non-newtonian.

Plasma is clearly more viscous than water secondary to its composition and therefore its relative viscosity must be higher than that of water (1.7).

Larger arterioles present the greatest resistance to flow. This is because there are fewer vessels in parallel and a greater proportion in series, leading to greater summation of resistance.

The decreased viscosity of blood in small vessels is because the red cells occupy the axial, central, fast-moving stream allowing plasma to flow slowly near the walls.

**3.47    The following statements are correct relating to cardiac physiology:**

☐   A   Mean arterial blood pressure (MABP) is calculated as diastolic blood pressure $+ \frac{1}{2}$ (systolic pressure – diastolic pressure)

☐   B   Arterial pulse pressure $= \frac{1}{3}$ (systolic pressure – diastolic pressure)

☐   C   Following ventricular contraction only one-third of ejected blood flows directly to the tissue; the remainder remains in the aorta

☐   D   Arteries contain 40% of the circulating blood volume

☐   E   Pulmonary capillary wedge pressure (PCWP) is needed to calculate left ventricular stroke work

### 3.47 Answers:

- A  False
- B  False
- C  True
- D  False
- E  True

Arterial pulse pressure is systolic blood pressure – diastolic blood pressure.

MABP is diastolic $+ \frac{1}{3}$ (systolic pressure – diastolic pressure).

Upon ventricular contraction only a small proportion of blood is propelled into the arteries/tissues; the remainder remains within the aorta and acts to distend their elastic walls. This is because of high impedance to flow but is important as it produces continuing flow of blood (the Windkessel effect, see Question 3.5).

Arteries contain 15% of circulating blood volume.

Left ventricular stroke work $=$ SV $\times$ (MABP – mean PCWP) $\times$ 0.0136

where SV – stroke volume.

**3.48    Regarding the control of arteriolar smooth muscle tone:**

F  ☐  A  A rising pressure causes relaxation of the muscular wall

T  ☐  B  Local metabolic control may be responsible for the hyperaemia seen after blood flow to an organ is temporarily stopped

T  ☐  C  Kallikreins indirectly cause relaxation of vascular smooth muscle

F  ☐  D  Thromboxane $A_2$ is a vasodilator

F  ☐  E  Epinephrine causes predominantly vasoconstriction in all organs

**3.48    Answers:**

- A  False
- B  True
- C  True
- D  False
- E  False

Smooth muscle in the arterioles spontaneously contracts in response to an increase in pressure within the vessel.

The increase in blood flow to an organ after a decrease in perfusion is known as reactive hyperaemia. Active hyperaemia is that observed with increasing tissue activity.

Thromboxane $A_2$ is a powerful vasoconstrictor and platelet aggregator.

Epinephrine acts on $\alpha$-receptors causing vasoconstriction and on $\beta_2$-receptors causing vasodilatation. The balance of receptor stimulation determines the overall response.

Kallikrein is responsible for activation of inactive kinins to active forms that cause smooth muscle relaxation.

**3.49    Regarding fetal circulation:**

□ A  The $P_{50}$ value for fetal haemoglobin is less than 3.6 kPa

□ B  The partial pressure of oxygen in the umbilical vein is approximately 8 kPa

□ C  A tissue flap known as the eustachian valve directs highly oxygenated blood across the foramen ovale into the left atrium

□ D  50% of the right ventricular ejectate enters the pulmonary circulation

□ E  The left ventricle receives approximately 65% of the venous return

**3.50    The effects of posture on the venous system include:**

□ A  A decrease in hydrostatic venous pressure in the leg on standing

□ B  A reduction in the arterial and venous pressure in the brain by approximately 50 mmHg on standing

□ C  The collapse of cerebral venous sinuses on standing

□ D  The rhythmic contraction of skeletal muscle in the legs to reduce venous blood volume while standing

□ E  The bi-directional flow of blood through the venous valves in the lower limbs while standing

65

**3.49 Answers:**

- A True
- B False
- C True
- D False
- E False

The $P_{50}$ of adult haemoglobin is higher than that of fetal blood. Therefore, fetal blood is able to obtain oxygen from maternal blood (see diagram in Answer 3.13). The umbilical vein transports blood from the placenta to the fetus. The partial pressure of oxygen in the umbilical vein is approximately 4.7 kPa (~80% saturated).

The pulmonary vascular resistance is high and therefore only approximately 12% of the right ventricle output enters the pulmonary circulation. The left ventricle receives only approximately 35% of total venous return.

Reference: The fetal circulation. *Continuing Education in Anaesthesia, Critical Care and Pain* 2005; 5(4): 107–12.

**3.50 Answers:**

- A False
- B True
- C False
- D True
- E False

Standing obviously increases venous hydrostatic pressure of the leg secondary to gravitational forces. On standing the CSF pressure also falls, so maintaining a relatively constant cerebral venous transmural pressure. The cerebral vein sinuses are also held open by extravascular tissue even when the intravascular pressure falls, hence the high risk for air embolus in sitting position for cranial surgery.

Unidirectional valves ensure that venous leg drainage returns to the heart.

**3.51 Valsalva's manoeuvre:**

*F* ☐ A Is performed by forced expiration against a closed glottis to a
pressure of 40 cmH$_2$O for 10 seconds *mmHg*

F ☐ B Phase 1 causes an increase in heart rate

T ☐ C Phase 2 results in an increase in heart rate

T ☐ D Phase 3 results from a sudden fall in intrathoracic pressure

F ☐ E A square-wave response may be seen in hypovolaemia

**3.51   Answers:**

- A  False
- B  False
- C  True
- D  True
- E  False

Valsalva's manoeuvre is a common physiological phenomenon on which to be questioned.

There are four phases resulting from changes in intrathoracic pressure.

The initial force is 40 mmHg not cmH$_2$O.

Phase 1 results from an increase in intrathoracic pressure causing a brief rise in blood pressure, with an accompanying fall in heart rate.

Phase 2 results from increase in intrathoracic pressure causing decrease venous return. To maintain cardiac output the heart rate increases.

With a sudden fall in intrathoracic pressure, having released the pressure in phase 3, there is a transient fall in blood pressure with a rise in heart rate.

Phase 4 results in overshoot as compensatory mechanisms continue to operate despite restoration of venous return.

As square wave is seen in cardiac failure, constrictive pericarditis or tamponade.

An exaggeration in fall in blood pressure is observed with hypovolaemia.

**3.52    Regarding cardiovascular responses to exercise:**

- □  A  The initial rise in heart rate is secondary to a reduction in vagal tone
- □  B  Blood flow to the brain increases
- □  C  There is a linear increase in stroke volume as exercise increases
- □  D  When exercise stops there is an abrupt decrease in cardiac output
- □  E  Diastolic blood pressure may fall during exercise

**3.52    Answers:**

- A   True
- B   False
- C   False
- D   True
- E   True

Initially a reduction in vagal tone leads to an increase in heart rate. Latterly the tachycardia is driven by sympathetic response.

Blood flow to the brain is constant no matter what the level of exercise.

There is a linear increase in heart rate to a maximum but the increase in stroke value is non-linear. There is a maximum increase in stroke volume occurring with light-to-moderate exercise and only a small further increment with strenuous exercise.

The sudden fall in cardiac output at the cessation of exercise is secondary to the loss of the muscle pump causing a decrease in venous return, along with a loss of motor cortical and sensory nerve activity associated with movement.

Diastolic blood pressure rises only slightly during exercise and may even fall. Systolic blood pressure rises in a non-linear fashion.

**3.53    Regarding cardiovascular response to haemorrhage:**

☐   A   With a 10% blood loss the pulse pressure is normal

☐   B   Compensatory mechanisms become inadequate to maintain
          cardiac output once 20% of blood loss has occurred

☐   C   Sympathetic stimulation is maximal within 30 seconds of
          haemorrhage

☐   D   Lactic acidosis caused by hypovolaemia causes an increase in
          peripheral vascular responses to catecholamines

☐   E   Decrease in stretch of the right atrium causes an increase in
          atrial natriuretic factor

**3.54    Regarding venous admixture:**

☐   A   There are no normal sources of anatomical shunts

☐   B   The effect of shunt is greater on the arterial partial pressure of
          oxygen than on the arterial oxygen content

☐   C   Shunt greatly affects arterial partial pressure of $CO_2$

☐   D   The shunt equation reads: $\dot{Q}s/\dot{Q}T = (Cc O_2 - Ca O_2) \div (Cc O_2 - C\bar{v}O_2)$

☐   E   $Cc O_2$ is measured from blood samples

71

**3.53   Answers:**

- A  False
- B  True
- C  True
- D  False
- E  False

With a 10% blood loss the pulse pressure is reduced but the mean arterial pressure may be normal.

Lactic acidosis causes myocardial depression and reduces the peripheral vascular responses to catecholamines.

Decrease in stretch of the right atrium leads to a decrease in atrial natriuretic factor release, which leads to an increase in antidiuretic hormone.

**3.54   Answers:**

- A  False
- B  True
- C  False
- D  True
- E  False

Thebesian veins draining the walls of the left ventricle and the veins draining bronchial circulation are both anatomical shunts.

Owing to the shape of the haemoglobin–oxygen dissociation curve there is relatively little reduction in oxygen content of blood, unlike that of dissolved oxygen.

Arterial partial pressure of carbon dioxide is not greatly affected by the shunt secondary to the steeper carbon dioxide–haemoglobin dissociation curve and the ventilatory responses secondary to an increase in carbon dioxide.

When using the shunt equation, $Cco_2$ or oxygen concentration of end-capillary blood, is calculated using the alveolar gas equation (to calculate alveolar partial pressure of oxygen) and the oxygen dissociation curve.

**3.55   Regarding the osmolar gap and osmolarity:**

☐   A   Osmolar gap is a measure of significant cations minus significant anions

☐   B   Osmolarity is calculated by $2 \times Na^+$ + glucose + urea (in milliosmoles per litre)

☐   C   The normal value for the osmolar gap is less than 10 mOsm/l

☐   D   Decreased serum water causes an increase in the osmolar gap

☐   E   Ethanol increases the osmolar gap

**3.56   The following are true regarding acid–base:**

☐   A   In metabolic acidosis the predicted $Pa_{CO_2}$ in mmHg is approximately calculated using the formula $0.7[HCO_3^-] + 20(\pm2)$ mmHg

☐   B   Uraemia is not a cause of a high anion gap

☐   C   Type A lactic acidosis by definition occurs in the presence of tissue hypoxia

☐   D   Type B lactic acidosis can occur because of defects in the tricarboxylate cycle.

☐   E   Peripheral venous bicarbonate is usually within 2–4 mmol/l of arterial bicarbonate

**3.55   Answers:**

- A   False
- B   True
- C   True
- D   True
- E   True

The osmolar gap is the difference between measured and calculated osmolarity, which is normally is less than 10 mosmol.

Causes of an increased osmolar gap include laboratory error, decreased serum water content, eg high lipids and high proteins, and additional low-molecular-weight substances in serum, eg methanol, glycine, ethanol or isoniazid.

**3.56   Answers:**

- A   True
- B   False
- C   True
- D   True
- E   True

A high anion gap can be secondary to lactic acidosis, ketoacidosis, uraemia or the presence of other organic acids, eg salicylates, methanol, ethyl glycol poisoning.

Type A lactic acidosis occurs in tissue hypoxia, although type B lactic acidosis occurs with normal tissue oxygenation but abnormal lactate utilisation, eg systemic disorders, drugs and heredity metabolic disorders. Any condition causing accumulation of pyruvate, including errors in the tricarboxylate cycle or the electron transport chain, can cause a type B lactic acidosis.

Peripheral venous bicarbonate is usually slightly higher than the arterial one.

Reference: Lactate physiology in health and disease. *Continuing Education in Anaesthesia, Critical Care and Pain* 2006; 6(3): 128–32.

**3.57** **When comparing a peripheral venous blood sample with an arterial blood sample (taken from the same patient at the same time):**

☐ A $PO_2$ is similar in both samples

☐ B $PCO_2$ is very different in the venous compared with the arterial sample

☐ C pH is similar in both samples

☐ D $HCO_3^-$ concentration is very different in the venous compared with the arterial sample

☐ E Measured potassium will not vary between the samples

**3.58** **Causes of a normal anion gap metabolic acidosis include:**

☐ A Vomiting

☐ B Distal renal tubular acidosis

☐ C Proximal renal tubular acidosis

☐ D Salicylate poisoning

☐ E Type B lactic acidosis secondary to heredity metabolic disorders

**3.57  Answers:**

- A  False
- B  False
- C  True
- D  False
- E  True

Peripheral venous pH compares favourably with arterial pH.

Venous $CO_2$ also compares favourably with arterial $CO_2$, although it is on average 0.8 kPa higher than the arterial one.

Peripheral venous bicarbonate is usually within 2–4 mmol/l of the arterial concentration.

**3.58  Answers:**

- A  True
- B  True
- C  True
- D  False
- E  False

Normal anion gap metabolic acidosis is secondary to:

- loss of bicarbonate, eg vomiting, gastrointestinal or renal causes
- failure to excrete hydrogen ions, eg distal renal tubular acidosis
- administration of hydrogen ions. eg total parenteral nutrition.

Salicylate poisoning gives a wide anion gap metabolic acidosis with a respiratory alkalosis and lactic acidosis gives a high anion gap.

To calculate anion gap:

$([Na^+] + [K^+]) - ([Cl^-] + [HCO_3^-])$

**3.59   When using a nerve simulator for peripheral nerve localisation:**

☐   A   The rheobase refers to the smallest current that is required to stimulate a nerve

☐   B   The chronaxy is the length of the current stimulus required to stimulate a nerve at twice its rheobase

☐   C   With a longer duration of nerve stimulation there is an increased likelihood of stimulating pain fibres

☐   D   Aα-fibre stimulation is associated with pain

☐   E   C-fibres are stimulated before δ-fibres with lengthening nerve stimulation

## 3.59 Answers:

- A True
- B True
- C True
- D False
- E False

| Fibre | Chronaxy (ms) |
|-------|---------------|
| $A\alpha$ | 0.05−0.1 |
| $A\delta$ | 0.15 |
| C | 0.4 |

As can be seen with increasing chronaxy there is an increasing likelihood of painful stimulation.

Pulse duration of 0.3 ms enables selective stimulation of motor fibres with minimal pain stimulus.

Reference: Electrical nerve locators. *Continuing Education in Anaesthesia, Critical Care and Pain* 2006; 6(1): 32−6.

**3.60    Regarding nerve stimulator settings for peripheral nerve
blockade:**

☐   A   A frequency of 10 Hz enables fast localisation of the nerve

☐   B   A twitch with current amplitude of less than 0.2 mA is desired

☐   C   The needle should ideally be connected to the cathode

☐   D   Higher amplitude settings are required for twitch visualisation
in paralysed patients

☐   E   The nerve stimulator should be equipped with a patient
indicator to illustrate delivered current

**3.60    Answers:**

- A  False
- B  False
- C  True
- D  False
- E  True

A frequency of 1–2 Hz, ie 1–2 beats per second, is used to enable direction of the nerve blockade needle.

Twitch with a current amplitude less than 0.2 mA may indicate that the needle is intraneural. However, twitch loss before 0.6 mA may mean that the needle tip is outside the nerve sheath.

Less current is required to stimulate a nerve when the cathode is adjacent to the nerve and the anode is distal. A patient indicator is an important safety feature. If current is not being delivered it will prevent potential trauma to the nerve.

If a patient is paralysed a twitch will not be seen.

## 3.61 Functions of the kidney include:

☐ A  Gluconeogenesis

☐ B  Production of cholecalciferol

☐ C  Renin production

☐ D  Angiotensinogen production

☐ E  Long-term regulation of blood volume

## 3.62 When assessing body fluid distribution:

☐ A  Interstitial water is less than half intracellular water

☐ B  Tritium ($^3H$) can be used to estimate total body water

☐ C  Markers used to determine extracellular fluid must cross capillaries but not cell membranes

☐ D  Thiosulphate is used to measure total body water

☐ E  Intracellular volume can be measured

66%.          30L          12L    3L

**3.61    Answers:**

- A  True
- B  False
- C  True
- D  False
- E  True

Vitamin D is derived from cholecalciferol (vitamin $D_3$) and is produced in the skin from 7-dehydrocholesterol in UV light. It is hydroxylated in the liver to form 25-hydroxycholecalciferol, which is then converted in the kidneys to the active form, 1,25-dihydroxycholecalciferol.

In starvation the kidneys are able to produce glucose from amino acids.

Renin is synthesised in the granular cells of the juxtaglomerular apparatus.

Angiotensinogen is a protein produced in the liver.

**3.62    Answers:**

- A  True
- B  True
- C  True
- D  False
- E  False

In a 70 kg man, 42 l is the estimated total body water content, of which 3 l is intravascular, 11 l interstitial and 28 l intracellular.

To estimate intravascular volume, markers that remain within the vessel must be used, eg albumin. To determine extracellular fluid see option D; inulin and thiosulphate are used.

Interstitial fluid volume cannot be directly measured. It is calculated by subtraction of plasma volume from extracellular volume. Intracellular volume must be derived.

**3.63    The proximal tubule of the kidney:**

☒  A  Reabsorbs ~40% of the filtrate

☐  B  Reabsorbs glucose

☐  C  Secretes ammonium

☒  D  Secretes bicarbonate

☒  E  Absorbs filtered protein

**3.64    Regarding renal blood flow:**

☐  A  It accounts for 20% of cardiac output

☐  B  A rise in perfusion pressure in the kidney leads to a fall in afferent arterial tone

☐  C  It is increased by an increase in sympathetic nerve activity

☐  D  Renal sympathetic activity increases glomerular capillary hydrostatic pressure

☐  E  Noradrenergic activity decreases afferent arteriole tone

### 3.63  Answers:

- A  False
- B  True
- C  True
- D  False
- E  True

The proximal tubule reabsorbs approximately 60% of its filtrate including water, sodium, chloride, potassium, bicarbonate, calcium, glucose, urea, phosphate and filtered proteins. It secretes (into the lumen from blood) hydrogen ions, ammonium ions, urate and organic anions and cations.

### 3.64  Answers:

- A  True
- B  False
- C  False
- D  True
- E  False

As perfusion pressure in the kidney rises, it causes increased stretching of the afferent arteriole secondary to an increase in transmural pressure; this causes a contraction of the afferent arteriole–the myogenic mechanism.

Noradrenergic stimulation of α-receptors causes constriction of both afferent and efferent arterioles. This causes a reduction in renal blood flow.

The sympathetic system affects glomerular filtration in two ways. It causes an increase in glomerular capillary hydrostatic pressure, which favours filtration. However, it causes a decrease in renal blood flow, which increases the glomerular capillary oncotic pressure and therefore, overall, slightly reduces glomerular filtration.

**3.65    Regarding the tubuloglomerular apparatus:**

□ A  The macula densa lies in the walls of the afferent arteriole

□ B  Adenosine released from the macula densa causes afferent arteriole vasoconstriction

□ C  An increase in sodium and chloride content is detected by the granular cells

□ D  Direct $\beta_1$ effect causes renin secretion from the juxtaglomerular apparatus

□ E  Mesangial cells are capable of phagocytosis

**3.66    Renin:**

□ A  Is produced by the granular cells

□ B  Is a proteolytic enzyme

□ C  Splits angiotensinogen to form angiotensin I

□ D  Production increases secondary to a decrease in sodium delivery to the macula densa

□ E  Is the rate-limiting enzyme in the conversion of angiotensinogen to angiotensin II

**3.65 Answers:**

- A False
- B True
- C False
- D True
- E True

The juxtaglomerular apparatus comprises the granular cells (renin production) found in the walls of the afferent arteriole.

The macula densa is a thickened portion of the wall of the ascending limb of the loop of Henle. It is involved in the control of renin production and renal blood flow. This area senses an increase in sodium and chloride, which leads to more adenosine release and so a reduction in glomerular filtration rate (GFR). It releases more adenosine if renal perfusion pressure rises.

The mesangial cells are located between capillaries. They are modified smooth muscle cells with contractile properties, and so they are able to aid blood flow regulation as they are continuous with the vascular smooth muscle cells. They can also produce a variety of cytokines and are capable of phagocytosis.

**3.66 Answers:**

- A True
- B True
- C True
- D True
- E True

Renin causes splitting of angiotensinogen (found mainly in the liver) to angiotensin I, which is a 10-amino acid peptide.

An increase in renin production is caused by a decrease in body sodium, decrease in circulating blood volume, increase in sympathetic activity and a decrease in afferent arteriole pressure.

**3.67    Angiotensin II:**

☐    A    Constricts afferent and efferent arterioles

☐    B    Causes a reduction in filtration coefficient of the renal
corpuscle

☐    C    Has no direct effect on renal tubules

☐    D    Indirectly affects the hypothalamus

☐    E    Stimulates ADH secretion

**3.68    The following are true of the physiology of the cyclo-oxygenase
enzymes:**

☐    A    Phospholipase $A_2$ catalyses the release of arachidonic acid
from phospholipids in cell membranes

☐    B    COX-1 is expressed only on specialist cells, including platelets
and renal tubule cells

☐    C    $PGE_2$ increases gastric acid secretion

☐    D    $PGI_2$ has a role in the maintenance of normal renal blood flow
in patients with renal dysfunction

☐    E    COX-1 is a major source of vascular $PGI_2$ biosynthesis

**3.67**   **Answers:**

- A   True
- B   True
- C   False
- D   False
- E   True

Constriction of afferent and efferent arterioles causes a decrease in renal blood flow.

Angiotensin II directly affects both tubules (causing fluid reabsorption) and the hypothalamus, increasing thirst and ADH secretion.

It also increases aldosterone production, is a vasoconstrictor and increases sympathetic nervous system activity, so leading to an increase in peripheral resistance and cardiac output.

**3.68**   **Answers:**

- A   True
- B   False
- C   False
- D   True
- E   False

COX-1 is expressed in most cells, not just specialised cells, but it is especially predominant in endothelial, platelet and renal tubular cells.

$PGE_2$ and -$I_2$ reduce gastric acid secretion, vasodilate mucosal vessels and increase mucus production.

COX-2 is a major source of vascular $PGI_2$ biosynthesis.

**3.69   Regarding COX enzymes:**

☐ A  Long-term inhibition of COX-2 is not associated with renal toxicity

☐ B  COX-2 is important for reproduction

☐ C  Long-term use of COX-1 inhibitors causes more gastrointestinal (GI) problems than does long-term COX-2 inhibition

☐ D  Peripheral COX-1 mediates nociception in rapidly developing pain

☐ E  COX-1 is needed for the platelet production of thromboxane

**3.70   Atrial natriuretic factor (ANF):**

☐ A  Is produced where there is lack of stretch of the atria

☐ B  Increases the glomerular hydrostatic pressure

☐ C  Is a powerful vasoconstrictor

☐ D  Causes afferent arteriole constriction

☐ E  Inhibits aldosterone release from the adrenal cortex

**3.69   Answers:**

- A   False
- B   True
- C   True
- D   False
- E   True

COX-1 and COX-2 inhibitors are associated with renal toxicity in susceptible individuals when used for long periods.

Peripheral COX-1 mediates nociception in slowly developing pain, whereas spinal COX-1 mediates nociception involved in rapidly developing pain.

COX-1 and COX-2 are important for fertility. COX-2 is expressed in cells of the reproductive tract and is needed for pregnancy. COX-1 is required for prostaglandin production, which maintains a healthy pregnancy.

**3.70   Answers:**

- A   False
- B   True
- C   False
- D   False
- E   True

ANF is released by atrial cells in response to stretching. It causes afferent arteriole dilatation and efferent arteriole constriction, so increasing glomerular hydrostatic pressure and increasing glomerular filtration rates. The overall result is diuresis. It also directly inhibits renin and aldosterone release and decreases sodium reabsorption in the collecting ducts.

**3.71   Regarding the loop of Henle:**

☐   A   The descending limb of the loop of Henle is impermeable to water

☐   B   The descending limb is impermeable to sodium and chloride

☐   C   The thick ascending limb is impermeable to water

☐   D   Active transport of sodium and chloride into the interstitial fluid increases the tubular osmolality in the ascending limb

☐   E   ADH affects water reabsorption in the thick ascending limb

**3.72   The following are true of the countercurrent exchanger:**

☐   A   It is an active process

☐   B   The blood flow in the vasa recta is fast flowing

☐   C   The osmolality at the base of the vasa recta is low

☐   D   Water leaves the descending vasa recta and enters the ascending vasa recta

☐   E   The descending vasa recta is permeable to urea

**3.71 Answers:**

- A False
- B True
- C True
- D False
- E False

The descending limb is permeable to water but impermeable to sodium and chloride.

Sodium and chloride are actively transported out of the thick ascending limb, causing a reduction in tubular osmolality and increase in interstitial osmolality. This draws water out of the descending limb. The overall effect is to cause fluid in the descending limb and the interstitial fluid to increase in osmolality.

ADH affects water uptake from the collecting ducts.

**3.72 Answers:**

- A False
- B False
- C False
- D True
- E True

The countercurrent exchanger is formed by a network of blood vessels, the vasa recta, which supply the loop of Henle and the collecting ducts. As the blood vessels descend into the medulla water is lost, which enters the ascending limb. Solutes are absorbed into the descending limb of the vasa recta from the ascending vasa recta. This ensures that the concentration gradient in the interstitial medulla is not washed away.

The osmolality at the top of the vasa recta is approximately 300 mosmol/kg $H_2O$ compared with that at the bottom, which is approximately 1200 mosmol/kg $H_2O$. It is a passive process resulting from the movement of water and solutes between the limbs of the slow-flowing blood in the vasa recta.

**3.73    Regarding urea and urine production:**

☐  A  Urea is partly responsible for the high medullary osmolality

☐  B  The distal convoluted tubule is impermeable to urea

☐  C  ADH stimulates absorption of urea into the medullary interstitium

☐  D  At times of water excess the collecting ducts are relatively impermeable to water

☐  E  In extreme conditions, urine can be as concentrated as 2000 mosmol/kg $H_2O$

**3.74    Acid–base control in the kidney:**

☐  A  Under normal circumstances all of the bicarbonate in the glomerular filtrate is absorbed

☐  B  Most bicarbonate is absorbed in the proximal tubule

☐  C  Bicarbonate is actively absorbed from the tubules in exchange for chloride ions

☐  D  The minimum urine pH is 6.1

☐  E  Filtered phosphate ions enable hydrogen ions to be excreted in the urine

**3.73   Answers:**

- A  True
- B  True
- C  True
- D  True
- E  False

Urea is essential for normal renal function. The loop of Henle, distal convoluted tubule, collecting ducts and outer medullary collecting ducts are impermeable to urea. This results in a higher urea concentration within the inner medullary collecting ducts. In times of water deprivation ADH stimulates urea reabsorption into the interstitial fluid. This promotes a concentrated osmolality favouring water reabsorption. It also increases water permeability of the collecting ducts, again facilitating water absorption.

The obligatory urine loss requires a urine osmolality of 1400 mosmol/kg $H_2O$.

**3.74   Answers:**

- A  True
- B  True
- C  False
- D  False
- E  True

A total of 85% of bicarbonate ions are reabsorbed in the proximal tubule. Most of the remaining bicarbonate is absorbed by the thick ascending limb of the loop of Henle.

The absorption of bicarbonate is not via active chloride exchange.

Hydrogen ions are secreted actively into the tubule whereupon they combine with filtered bicarbonate ions forming carbonic acid. This breaks down to form carbon dioxide and water, which then readily diffuse into the luminal cells. Once inside the cell, carbonic anhydrase catalyses the reaction of carbon dioxide with water to form bicarbonate ions (which are reabsorbed into the peritubular capillaries) and hydrogen ions (which can once again be secreted into the tubular lumen).

The minimal urinary pH is 4.4, below which the elevated hydrogen ions prevent any further hydrogen ion active transport.

**3.75    Regarding the renal response to disturbed acid–base:**

☐    A  In metabolic acidosis, ammonia combines with hydrogen ions within the lumen to enable renal hydrogen ion loss

☐    B  At urinary pH 4.4 further hydrogen ions can be lost by combination with ammonia in the lumen

☐    C  In metabolic acidosis the amount of filtered bicarbonate is reduced

☐    D  Low extracellular hydrogen ion concentration decreases tubular secretion of ammonia ions

☐    E  During metabolic acidosis there is increased hydrogen secretion from tubule cells into the lumen

### 3.75    Answers:

- A  True
- B  True
- C  True
- D  True
- E  True

Deamination of glutamine in the proximal tubule, the thick ascending limb of the loop of Henle and the distal tubules causes the formation of two ammonium ions, $NH_4^+$ and two bicarbonate ions, $HCO_3^-$. Ammonium ions are actively secreted into the lumen in exchange for sodium ions. The bicarbonate is absorbed into the blood, therefore decreasing the metabolic acidosis.

Further along the nephron, ammonia ($NH_3$), which is lipid soluble, diffuses from the interstitial fluid into the collecting duct cells and then into the collecting duct tubule lumen. Here it combines with hydrogen ions to form $NH_4^+$, which is ionised and therefore trapped and so excreted. This reaction can even occur in the most acidic urine, thereby increasing hydrogen ion excretion in extreme metabolic acidosis.

In metabolic acidosis there is a decrease in blood bicarbonate, so less is filtered. Low extracellular hydrogen ions occur in alkalotic states where there would be no benefit in increasing hydrogen ion excretion. Therefore, there would be no benefit in causing an increase in tubular ammonium ion secretion.

**3.76    Regarding acute haemolytic transfusion reactions:**

- ☐ A  Signs may occur after transfusion of only 5 ml of incompatible blood
- ☐ B  It can occur secondary to anti-RhE in the recipient's blood
- ☐ C  It can occur secondary to Kell's antibodies in the recipient's blood
- ☐ D  Jk (Kidd) antigens can be causative, which are difficult to detect in pre-transfusion samples
- ☐ E  It is likely to occur if a rhesus-positive AB recipient receives rhesus-negative A blood

**3.76    Answers:**

- A  True
- B  True
- C  True
- D  True
- E  False

Acute haemolytic transfusion reactions can occur after transfusion of only 5–10 ml of incompatible blood. Other than ABO incompatibility, there are a number of other red blood cell antibodies in the recipient's blood that can cause such a reaction including anti-RhD, -E and -C and Kell's antibodies. Reactions to these are usually less severe than the ABO reaction as complement is not activated. However, reactions to Jk (Kidd) and Fy (Duffy) antigens do activate complement and can cause severe transfusion reactions, leading to renal and cardiac failure.

AB blood group has neither A nor B antibodies and is said to be a universal acceptor.

Reference: McClelland B. *Handbook of Transfusion Medicine.* 2nd edn. Blood Transfusion Services of the United Kingdom, 1996.

**3.77    Regarding blood groups:**

☐   A   In the white population the AB blood group is the most infrequent

☐   B   The naturally occurring antibodies, eg anti-A in a blood group B patient, are mostly IgM

☐   C   The persistent immune antibodies developing on exposure to foreign red cells are IgG

☐   D   IgM antibodies pass transplacentally

☐   E   Small amounts of group A and B antigens can enter the body in food and bacteria

**3.78    Regarding granulocytes:**

☐   A   Neutrophils are attracted to inflamed areas by chemicals released by damaged tissues

☐   B   Opsonisation occurs when foreign particles are labelled with immunoglobulin or complement

☐   C   Eosinophils circulate in the peripheral circulation for most of their life span

☐   D   Eosinophils are not phagocytic

☐   E   Eosinophils release enzymes that inhibit mass cell products

**3.77  Answers:**
- A  True
- B  True
- C  True
- D  False
- E  True

In the white population the following percentages of blood group are seen:

- A group     45%
- B group     9%
- AB group    3%
- O group     43%.

Naturally occurring antibodies are reactive at 37°C but optimally reactive at 4°C, unlike immune antibodies, which are optimally reactive at 37°C.

The immune antibodies are IgG antibodies but IgM antibodies may also develop in the early phase of the reaction.

Only IgG antibodies pass transplacentally.

**3.78  Answers:**
- A  True
- B  True
- C  False
- D  False
- E  True

Neutrophils and monocytes are also attracted to areas by complement or leukocyte cohesion molecule interaction with damaged tissue. They are also attracted towards bacteria.

Fc and C3b receptors on monocytes and neutrophils ensure recognition and subsequent phagocytosis of opsonised material.

Eosinophils circulate for up to 8 hours before entering into the tissues (predominantly epithelial lining). Their life span is approximately 8–12 days compared with 4–5 days for neutrophils. They phagocytose antigen–antibody complexes. They also have a role in reducing spread of inflammation by destroying immune complexes.

**3.79    Regarding white blood cells:**

☐  A  Basophils are involved in allergic reactions

☐  B  Basophils are predominantly found circulating in blood

☐  C  Basophils have predominantly IgG attachment sites

☐  D  Monocytes, on entering tissues, mature into mast cells

☐  E  Macrophages release tumour necrosis factor (TNF)

**3.80    Regarding lymphocytes:**

☐  A  Most circulating lymphocytes are B lymphocytes

☐  B  CD3 (part of the T-cell receptor) is present on all T cells

☐  C  T-helper lymphocytes possess a surface glycoprotein CD4

☐  D  CD4-surface glycoprotein binds to MHC class II molecules on antigen-presenting cells

☐  E  Helper T cells aid in the promotion of B-cell maturation

### 3.79    Answers:

- A   True
- B   False
- C   False
- D   False
- E   True

Basophils have cytoplasmic granules and contain active substances including histamine, serotonin, hyaluronic acid and heparin. They are occasionally present in blood but are predominantly tissue bound as in mast cells. They have IgE attachment sites and are important in allergic and parasitic conditions.

Monocytes mature to macrophages in tissues, where they can continue to function for years. They are phagocytic and have receptors for IgG, complement and various other lymphokines. As well as TNF, they can also produce interleukin-1 (IL-10), prostaglandins and interferon.

### 3.80    Answers:

- A   False
- B   True
- C   True
- D   True
- E   True

T cells account for 80% of circulating lymphocytes.

CD4 is present on the surface of T-helper cells and monocytes

Approximately 65% of the lymphocytes are T-helper lymphocytes. They promote antibody production and secrete interleukins, which cause B-lymphocyte proliferation and activation. They are inhibited by IL-10 and interferon.

Reference: Kalra P. *Lymphocytes. Essential Revision Notes for MRCP.* 2nd edn. PasTest Ltd., 2004.

**3.81    Regarding immunity:**

☐  A  Plasma cells are non-circulating B lymphocytes

☐  B  The majority of B lymphocytes express MHC class I antigens

☐  C  Suppressor or cytotoxic T cells express CD4 surface glycoproteins

☐  D  All B lymphocytes can secrete antibody

☐  E  Plasma cells produce antibodies

## 3.81    Answers:

- A  True
- B  False
- C  False
- D  False
- E  True

Plasma cells are non-circulating B lymphocytes in bone marrow, lymph nodes and gut. Plasma cells produce antibodies. Immature B lymphocytes are unable to secrete antibody. The majority of B lymphocytes express MHC class II antigens.

Suppressor or cytotoxic T cells express CD8 surface glycoproteins that interact with MHC class I molecules expressed on cells. This is important for destroying virally infected cells.

Cytotoxic T cells secrete cytokine interleukins (IL-2), interferon-$\alpha$ and tumour necrosis factor. They induce B lymphocytes and recruit activated immune cells to the area.

Immunoglobulins are made up of two fragments: the Fab fragment with antigen-binding capacities and the Fc fragment with the effector function.

**3.82    Regarding allergy:**

☐   A   Anaphylactoid reactions are a result of IgE-mediated hypersensitivity

☐   B   Most anaesthetic drug reactions are because of muscle relaxation

☐   C   Anaphylactoid reactions require a prior sensitisation

☐   D   Mast cell tryptase reaches its peak after approximately 6 hours

☐   E   Serum for mast cell tryptase should be frozen before analysis

## 3.82    Answers:

- A  False
- B  True
- C  False
- D  False
- E  False

Anaphylactoid reactions are non-immune. They are not IgE mediated and require no prior exposure to the allergen. They are mediated by direct histamine release from mast cells or complement activation.

Anaphylactic reactions require prior sensitisation and result in potential catastrophic IgE-mediated hypersensitivity.

Mast cell tryptase reaches its peak after 1 hour and should be refrigerated but not frozen before analysis, which should be ideally done within 48 hours.

Basophil cell surface markers may also help with anaphylaxis diagnosis. Although they have a high specificity, their sensitivity may be as low as 50%.

Also, remember that crossreactivity may occur. Patients with no previous anaesthetic exposure can be sensitive to agents secondary to other agents, eg cosmetics or over-the-counter medication and even cleaning products.

Reference: Anaphylaxis. *Continuing Education in Anaesthesia, Critical Care and Pain* 2004; 4(4): 111–13.

**3.83    The following are true, regarding life-threatening allergic reactions during anaesthesia:**

- ☐   A   Antibiotics are the second most common cause
- ☐   B   Gelatins are the commonest cause for colloid allergy
- ☐   C   Reactions to etomidate are more common than reactions to propofol
- ☐   D   Radiocontrast allergy does not typically present at the time of administration
- ☐   E   Benzodiazepines are more likely to cause allergy than opioids

### 3.83    Answers:

- A  False
- B  True
- C  False
- D  False
- E  True

Reactions to etomidate are rare. Common reactions to radiocontrast media include flushing, nausea and warmth. Hypersensitivity reactions can occur in 3% of patients and occur at the time of administration. Having suffered a reaction, the risk of allergy to subsequent exposure is markedly increased.

The table represents the spread of anaesthetic agents causing life-threatening allergic reactions.

| Agent | Percentage |
|---|---|
| Neuromuscular blocking agent | 70 |
| Latex | 12.6 |
| Colloids | 4.7 |
| Induction agents | 3.6 |
| Antibiotics | 2.6 |
| Others | 2.5 |
| Benzodiazepines | 2 |
| Opioids | 1.7 |

Reference: Anaphylaxis. *Continuing Education in Anaesthesia, Critical Care and Pain* 2004; 4(4): 111–13.

**3.84    Pain physiology:**

☐  A   Aδ-fibres conduct impulses at 5–10 m/s

☐  B   Aδ-fibres synapse at laminae II and III

☐  C   Dull pain travels in myelinated fibres

☐  D   Fast pain fibres ascend to the posterior thalamic nuclei

☐  E   Some C-fibres are silent unless stimulated by inflammatory
        conditions

**3.84    Answers:**

- A  False
- B  False
- C  False
- D  True
- E  True

Aδ-fibres (fast fibres) conduct impulses at 12–30 m/s. They are myelinated fibres that enter the dorsal horn of the spinal cord and synapse at laminae I, V and X. Conduction continues in the secondary afferent fibres via the neospinothalamic tract to the posterior thalamic nuclei.

C-fibres transmit dull pain or slow pain. The fibres conduct impulses at 0.5–2 m/s via unmyelinated fibres that synapse at laminae II and III (substantia gelatinosa) of the dorsal horn.

A total of 15% of C-fibres present in the skin and viscera are silent or dormant and become activated only during inflammatory conditions.

Reference: Anatomy, physiology and pharmacology of pain. *Anaesthesia and Intensive Care Medicine* 2005; 6: 7–10.

**3.85 Pain fibres:**

☐ A Fast pain is transmitted from the lamina to the thalamus via a monosynaptic pathway

☐ B Having synapsed in the laminae, the pain pathway for slow pain follows a monosynaptic pathway to the thalamus

☐ C Fast pain pathways are responsible for circulatory reflex responses to pain

☐ D Visceral nociceptors are very dense compared with somatic nociceptors

☐ E Visceral pain exhibits spatial summation

**3.85    Answers:**

- A   True
- B   False
- C   False
- D   False
- E   True

Dull or slow pain travels in C-fibres to laminae II and III where they synapse with second-order neurons that transmit information via a polysynaptic system to multiple regions, including the midbrain, pons, medulla and hypothalamus. This slow pain pathway is responsible for reflex response to pain (including respiratory, circulatory and endocrine responses).

Visceral nociceptors are much less densely placed than somatic nociceptors, which leads to poorly localised, diffuse and often midline pain.

Visceral pain exhibits spatial summation. If a large area is stimulated the pain threshold is lowered (not present in cutaneous nociceptors).

Reference: Anatomy, physiology and pharmacology of pain. *Anaesthesia and Intensive Care Medicine* 2005; 6: 7–10.

**3.86    Cerebrospinal fluid density:**

☐  A  Has a mean of 1.1000 g/l

☐  B  Is greater in women compared with men

☐  C  Is lower in pregnant compared with non-pregnant women

☐  D  Is lower in premenopausal compared with postmenopausal women

☐  E  Affects spread of intrathecal solutions

**3.86   Answers:**

- A  False
- B  False
- C  True
- D  True
- E  True

Mean CSF density is 1.0003 g/l with normal physiological range of 1–1.0006 ± 2 SD g/l.

CSF density is greater in men compared with women and in non-pregnant compared with pregnant women.

Baricity of injected intrathecal preparations, ie the ratio of density of injectate to the density of CSF, has a marked effect on spread.

Hypobaric solutions will cause a rise and hyperbaric solutions a fall.

Reference: Intrathecal drug spread. *British Journal of Anaesthesia* 2004; 93(4): 568–78.

**3.87    The following are functions of the vagus nerve:**

☐ A  Sensation to the epiglottis

☐ B  Bronchial mucus production

☐ C  Sensation to the dura

☐ D  Sensation to the external auditory meatus

☐ E  Bronchoconstriction in the lungs

**3.87    Answers:**

- A  True
- B  True
- C  True
- D  True
- E   True

The vagus nerve is motor, sensory and secretomotor. It has three nuclei: the dorsal nucleus that is mixed, the nucleus ambiguus, which is motor and the nucleus of tractus solitarius, which serves sensory functions including taste. It provides motor innervation to the larynx, via the recurrent laryngeal and to the bronchial and upper GI muscles up to the splenic flexure. It has a large sensory role including dura, external auditory meatus, respiratory tract, GI tract to the ascending colon, myocardium and epiglottis. Its secretomotor function includes bronchial mucus and alimentary tract.

Reference: Urquhart J, Blunt M. and Pinnock C. *The Anaesthesia Viva 1*. Greenwich Medical Media, 1996.

## 3.88   The following are true regarding classes of nerve fibres:

☐ A   Aβ-fibres are the largest

☐ B   B-fibres are efferent

☐ C   Spindle afferent fibres have the slowest velocity

☐ D   Dull pain fibres are the smallest

☐ E   Motor fibres are the fastest

## 3.88 Answers:

- A False
- B False
- C False
- D True
- E True

Aα-fibres are the largest at 12–20 mm with a velocity of 70–120 m/s and they supply somatic motor.

Aβ-fibres are 5–12 mm in diameter with a velocity of 30–70 m/s and serve touch, pressure and proprioception.

Aγ-fibres are 3–6 mm diameter with a velocity of 15–30 m/s and supply spindle afferent fibres.

Aδ-fibres are 2–5 mm with a velocity of 12–30 m/s and supply sharp pain and temperature.

B-fibres are <3 mm diameter with a velocity of 3–15 m/s and supply preganglionic autonomic fibres.

C-fibres are 0.4–1.2 mm with a velocity of 0.5–2 m/s and give rise to dull pain.

Reference: Urquhart J, Blunt M. and Pinnock C. *The Anaesthesia Viva 1*. Greenwich Medical Media, 1996.

**3.89    Regarding obstructive sleep apnoea:**

☐ A  It is referred to as sleep apnoea syndrome when the patient suffers with excess daytime somnolence

☐ B  In the absence of abnormal anatomy it occurs because of relaxation of the pharyngeal constrictor muscles while sleeping

☐ C  By definition the oxygen saturation must fall by 10% to meet the diagnostic criteria

☐ D  Nasal CPAP (continuous positive airway pressure) is the gold standard of treatment

☐ E  Morbid obesity alone is a predictor of difficult intubation

**3.90    The following are expected clinical signs for a fit young adult who has lost 20% intravascular blood volume:**

☐ A  Heart rate >140 beats/min

☐ B  Urine output is <1 ml/kg per hour

☐ C  Cool shutdown of peripheries

☐ D  Restlessness and irritation

☐ E  Normal blood pressure when supine

**3.89    Answers:**

- A  True
- B  True
- C  False
- D  True
- E  False

Obstructive sleep apnoea affects up to 5% of the UK population, 80% of whom are male. It is the repetitive obstruction of the upper airway during sleep, which leads to a decrease in arterial oxygen saturation. The diagnostic criteria quote a saturation reduction of at least 4%, with obstructive episodes lasting for >10 s. Obesity alone is not a predictor of difficulty of intubation; however, when combined with other scoring measures, eg Wilson scoring, it increases the predictive value.

Reference: Obstructive sleep apnoea and anaesthesia. *Anaesthesia and Intensive Care Medicine* 2005; 6: 225.

**3.90    Answers:**

- A  False
- B  True
- C  True
- D  False
- E  True

With 20% intravascular blood loss expected, clinical signs in a fit young adult include heart rate 100–120, orthostatic hypotension, reduced urine output <1 ml/kg per h, cool shutdown of peripheries and normal CNS.

Reference: Assessment of gastrointestinal problems. *Anaesthesia and Intensive Care Medicine* 2003; 4: 38–41.

**3.91    The following are true regarding the hormonal changes of pregnancy:**

☐ A  Growth hormone production is reduced

☐ B  Both free and total plasma cortisol increase

☐ C  Aldosterone increases because of the natriuretic effect of progesterone

☐ D  A high plasma concentration of free thyroxine is expected

☐ E  There is a reduction in prostaglandins during the first trimester

**3.92    Regarding maternal physiology during pregnancy:**

☐ A  The basal metabolic rate increases by 20% at 36 weeks

☐ B  Significant cardiovascular changes start to occur in the second trimester

☐ C  Colloid oncotic pressure increases during pregnancy

☐ D  Stroke volume increases by 20%

☐ E  Downregulation of $\alpha$-receptors contributes to the decrease in peripheral resistance

**3.91  Answers:**

- A  True
- B  True
- C  True
- D  False
- E  False

Growth hormone production is reduced. This is thought to happen because of an increase in the production of human placental lactogen from the placenta. Along with a rise in cortisol and aldosterone, renin and angiotensin concentrations also rise. Although there is a rise in thyroxine production, there is also a rise in the thyroid-binding globulin, such that the free thyroxine concentration is unchanged. Prostaglandin A increases threefold during the first trimester, which results in systemic vasodilatation. Prostaglandin E increases significantly during the third trimester.

**3.92  Answers:**

- A  True
- B  False
- C  False
- D  True
- E  True

A quick revision tip is that most physiological parameters increase by approximately 20% or 40% during pregnancy!

Basal metabolic rate and oxygen consumption increase by 20%. Significant cardiovascular changes occur early in the first trimester, with a 17% increase in heart rate occurring by week 12. Heart rate peaks in the middle of the third trimester at 25% above baseline. Stroke volume increases by 20% and this occurs predominantly by the end of the first trimester. Peripheral resistance decreases by 30–35%. This is because of progesterone, prostaglandins and downregulation of $\alpha$-receptors. Cardiac output increases by 50% by weeks 32–36.

**3.93    Maternal changes during pregnancy include:**
- ☐  A   An increase in renal blood flow of 20%
- ☐  B   Aortocaval compression occuring during the first trimester
- ☐  C   An increase in blood volume of approximately 1.5 l
- ☐  D   A marked reduction of diaphragmatic contraction at term
- ☐  E   A reduction in vital capacity of 30% at term

**3.93    Answers:**

- A  False
- B  False
- C  True
- D  False
- E  False

Renal blood increases 50% by the first trimester. Aortocaval compression becomes significant at approximately 20 weeks.

Although the diaphragm is displaced outwards, the contraction is unaffected. The lower ribs flare out, so increasing both the anterior-posterior (AP) and transverse diameters of the thorax. This is because of a reduction in ligamentous tone secondary to relaxin.

| Respiratory parameter | Effect of pregnancy (%) |
|---|---|
| Airway resistance | Decreases (35) |
| ERV | Decreases (20) |
| RV | Decreases (20) |
| FRC | Decreases (20) |
| TV | Increases (30) |
| IC | Increases (10) |
| EC | Decreases (20) |
| TLC | Decreases (5) |
| VC | Unchanged |
| Lung compliance | Unchanged |
| Total respiratory compliance | Decreases (20) |
| Anatomical dead space | Increases (45) |
| MV | Increases (50) |
| RR | Increases (10) |
| TV | Increases (40) |

**3.94** **The following is true regarding the physiological changes occurring during labour:**

☐ A  Each uterine contraction delivers approximately 300 ml of blood back to the maternal circulation

☐ B  Cardiac output increases by 45% during the expulsive phase

☐ C  Maternal diastolic pressure can be expected to increase by 20 mmHg during uterine contraction

☐ D  Uterine contractions increase the oxygen consumption by 20%

☐ E  The epidural pressure can increase by 60 cmH$_2$O during the second stage.

**3.94    Answers:**

- A  True
- B  True
- C  True
- D  False
- E  True

The combination of auto-transfusion and the reduction in pressure of the uterus on the inferior vena cava results in a massive increase in cardiac output immediately following delivery (to 60–80% greater than pre-labour values). Both systolic and diastolic pressures increase by 10–20 mmHg during contractions. Uterine contractions increase oxygen consumption by 60%. The CSF pressure is unchanged during pregnancy. Epidural pressure in pregnancy is slightly elevated at 1 cmH$_2$O, but is hugely elevated during a contraction.

**3.95 The following results are within normal limits for pregnancy:**

☐ A   $P$aCO$_2$ 3.46 kPa at 12 weeks' pregnancy

☐ B   Plasma bicarbonate 28 at term

☐ C   Base excess −6 at term

☐ D   Haematocrit 45% at term

☐ E   White cell count (WCC) 20 at term

**3.95    Answers:**

- A  True
- B  False
- C  False
- D  False
- E  False

It is important to realise that the normal ranges for some tests alter during pregnancy. However, do not assume that an abnormal test must be pregnancy related. As early as the eighth to tenth weeks, progesterone has stimulated the respiratory centre to produce maximal hyperventilation. This change causes a respiratory alkalosis with a $PaCO_2$ normal range of 3.46–4.26 kPa. Renal compensation decreases plasma bicarbonate to a normal range of 18–20 mmol/l and a base deficit of −2 to −3.

Red cell mass increases by 20%. Plasma volume increases by up to 50%, so haematocrit decreases to ~33–35%. Hb concentration at term is usually ~12 g/dl. Platelet count remains the same or decreases slightly by haemodilution. WCC much above $9 \times 10^3/mm^3$ is not thought to be normal (Note: think of infection or steroid therapy). Clotting factors increase throughout pregnancy, and fibrinolysis and fibrin formation increase as the pregnancy reaches term.

**3.96    Regarding fetal changes occurring at birth:**

☐  A  Clamping the umbilical cord increases systemic vascular resistance

☐  B  When right atrial pressure exceeds left atrial pressure the foramen ovale closes

☐  C  Physiological closure of the ductus arteriosus occurs at the same time as closure of the foramen ovale

☐  D  The initial decrease in the pulmonary vascular resistance is because of abolition of hypoxic pulmonary vasoconstriction

☐  E  Increasing levels of prostaglandins $E_1$ and $E_2$ cause closure of the ductus arteriosus

**3.96 Answers:**

- A True
- B False
- C False
- D False
- E False

Clamping the umbilical cord prevents flow of blood to the low resistance placenta and therefore the systemic vascular resistance (SVR) increases. This also causes an increase in left ventricular end-diastolic pressure. A reduction in flow to the inferior vena cava reduces the right atrial pressure. On taking the first breath, the lungs expand causing a huge decrease in pulmonary vascular resistance (PVR); this reduces right ventricular end-diastolic pressure.

PVR is further reduced by increasing arterial oxygen concentration and decreasing carbon dioxide concentration. Increased blood flow through the lungs causes an increase in left atrial pressure. When this pressure exceeds right atrial pressure, the foramen ovale closes. Permanent closure occurs at 4–6 weeks. The ductus arteriosus closes in response to increased arterial oxygen concentration and decreasing prostaglandins $E_1$ and $E_2$. Physiological closure occurs at 10–15 hours and permanent closure normally occurs at 2–3 weeks. The ductus venosus closes within hours of birth.

**3.97    Regarding thermoregulation:**

☐  A  The anterior hypothalamus is predominantly responsible for
       receiving afferent inputs about temperature

☐  B  The hypothalamus does not have actual thermoreceptors

☐  C  The posterior hypothalamus is responsible for the coordination
       of reflex responses to heat

☐  D  Non-shivering thermogenesis can increase heat production in
       infants by 200%

☐  E  Fever caused by pyogens is because of peripheral mechanism
       responses that are unable to match the hypothalamic set point

## 3.97 Answers:

- A True
- B False
- C False
- D True
- E False

Normal core body temperature ranges from 36 to 37.5°C. Afferent receptors from the skin, deep tissue and spinal cord pass via the brain stem to the preoptic nucleus of the anterior hypothalamus. The anterior hypothalamus also contains heat-sensitive neurons and receives additional thermal afferents from other areas of the brain. The posterior hypothalamus is responsible for coordination of responses to cold, ie vasoconstriction and shivering. The anterior hypothalamus is responsible for response to heat, ie vasodilatation and sweating. Non-shivering thermogenesis is the increase in cellular metabolism in brown cells, occurring in response to beta-sympathetic stimulation of circulating catecholamines. Adults lack brown fat and so this mechanism is responsible for at most a 15% increase in the rate of heat production. Infants, however, have significant brown fat and are able to increase their rate of heat production by up to 200%. Pyogens alter the set point of the hypothalamus, which then causes peripheral mechanism activation for heat production.

**3.98   Hypothermia:**

- ☐ A   May be more extreme with a regional anaesthetic technique (RA) compared with a general anaesthetic (GA)
- ☐ B   Causes decreased activation of the coagulation cascade
- ☐ C   Of 28°C is associated with a reduction in cerebral metabolic rate by 50%
- ☐ D   Has no effect on the triggering of malignant hyperthermia
- ☐ E   Causing shivering is caused by both peripheral and central mechanisms

**3.98    Answers:**

- A  True
- B  True
- C  True
- D  False
- E  True

During a GA tonic vasoconstriction is attenuated; this results in the early decrease in core temperature, with the loss of the core-peripheral gradient. Gradually heat loss reduces as a balance is reached between heat loss and heat production. Should the patient become sufficiently hypothermic, the attenuated vasoconstrictive response will activate. Shivering is rare as the vasoconstriction normally maintains core temperature. During RA, the initial heat loss because of attenuation of tonic vasoconstriction is reduced as only the blocked area is affected. However, the patient remains unable to vasoconstrict in the blocked area. This may cause heat loss such that shivering is triggered. Even then, only the unblocked areas are able to generate heat. The combination of GA and RA is the worst for heat loss. Coagulation is also affected, as platelet function is impaired. Hypothermia delays the trigger of malignant hyperthermia. Shivering is involuntary muscle contraction, consisting of rapid tremors under peripheral control and slow synchronous waves under central control. Interestingly, for each litre of fluid infused at ambient temperature, the mean core body temperature will fall by $\sim$0.25 °C.

Reference: Stoelting RK, Hillier SC. *Pharmacology and Physiology in Anesthetic Practice*. 4th edn. Lippincott, Williams & Wilkins, 2005.

**3.99  The physiology of old age. In elderly people:**

☐  A  Atrial contraction contributes less to ventricular filling

☐  B  A normal ejection fraction as diagnosed on echocardiography excludes the diagnosis of diastolic dysfunction

☐  C  Diastolic pressure increases more than systolic pressure.

☐  D  There is a reduction in the release of endothelial nitric oxide

☐  E  Circulating norepinephrine concentrations are decreased

**3.99    Answers:**

- A  False
- B  False
- C  False
- D  True
- E  False

Atrial contraction accounts or ~30% of ventricular filling compared to 10% in young people, this is because of impaired relaxation of cardiac fibres as a result of diastolic dysfunction. A normal ejection fraction gives no indication of diastolic function. Thickening of the intima and media within the vessels leads to enhanced pulse wave propagation in elderly people. A higher systolic pressure is seen as a result. Diastolic pressure increases to a lesser extent. In young people the cushioning effect of the walls of the vessels delays the return of the pulse wave, giving a lower systolic and a higher diastolic pressure. Nitric oxide is a vasodilator. Its release in all vascular beds is reduced in elderly people. Circulating norepinephrine increases with age. There is decreased reuptake at nerve endings, reduction in sensitivity at the receptors and reduction in contractile response.

References: Physiology of ageing. *Anaesthesia and Intensive Care Medicine* 2003; 4: 337–8.

Perioperative care of the elderly. *Continuing Education in Anaesthesia, Critical Care and Pain* 2004; 4(6): 193–6.

**3.100  In elderly people:**

□  A  The decline in heart rate response to exercise is because of receptor downregulation

□  B  Orthostatic hypotension rarely coexists with hypertension

□  C  A restrictive respiratory pattern is seen with decreasing chest wall mobility

□  D  Functional reserve capacity (FRC) increases by 3% per decade

□  E  Hepatic enzyme function reduces

## 3.100   Answers:

- A  True
- B  False
- C  True
- D  True
- E  False

Downregulation of β-receptors causes the reduction in maximum heart rate. Impaired baroreceptor function and peripheral vasoconstrictor responses are responsible for postural hypotension. This can be even more marked in the hypertensive patient taking salt-wasting pharmacological agents such as diuretics. A less compliant chest wall with decreased costochondral mobility is seen. The lung tissue lacks elasticity and changes similar to those seen in emphysema develop. There is also an increase in the closing volume, with reduced alveolar surface area, alveolar wall thickening, $\dot{V}/\dot{Q}$ mismatching and marked reduction in gas exchange. Expected $PaO_2$ can be calculated according to the equation: $13.6 - (0.044 \times age)$ kPa.

TLC and FRC reduce and ERV and RV increase. Hepatic blood flow reduces but enzyme function is preserved.

References: *Pharmacology and Physiology in Anesthetic Practice.* Fourth Edition. K. Stoelting.

Physiology of ageing. *Anaesthesia and Intensive Care Medicine* 2003; 4: 337–8.

**3.101  Regarding lymphatics:**

- ☐  A  They are absent from CNS tissues
- ☐  B  Their main function is to remove protein from interstitial fluid
- ☐  C  They are valveless vessels
- ☐  D  They normally have a protein concentration of $\sim$1.8 g/dl
- ☐  E  From the right lymphatic duct they can drain into the innominate veins

**3.101  Answers:**

- A  True
- B  True
- C  False
- D  True
- E  True

Bone, cartilage, epithelium and CNS tissues have no lymphatic vessels. The lymphatic vessels have one-way valves that allow flow of fluid and protein only away from the interstitium. The left-sided thoracic duct drains into the venous system at the junction between the left internal jugular and the left subclavian vein. The right lymphatic duct sometimes is not even present. It is formed from three lymphatic vessels, which can drain separately into the right internal jugular, subclavian vein and innominate veins.

**3.102   The following are true of hypothalamic and pituitary physiology:**

☐   A   The hypothalamus can be stimulated only by substances that cross the blood–brain barrier.

☐   B   The posterior pituitary is the site of synthesis of oxytocin

☐   C   Anxiety and stress of anaesthesia stimulate the release of growth hormone

☐   D   Growth hormone increases the utilisation of glucose by muscles

☐   E   Prolactin is a potent inhibitor of ovarian function

### 3.102 Answers:

- A False
- B False
- C True
- D False
- E True

The hypothalamus is located outside the blood–brain barrier and therefore is able to respond to circulating stimulants including sodium and cortisol. The pituitary gland is also situated outside the blood–brain barrier. The posterior pituitary stores and secretes oxytocin and ADH, but these are synthesised in the hypothalamus (in the paraventricular and supraoptic nuclei respectively). Growth hormone secretion is stimulated by sleep, hypoglycaemia, fasting, $\alpha$ agonists, oestrogen, amino acid increase and free fatty acid decrease.

The actions of growth hormone include increased protein synthesis and mobilisation of free fatty acids. It also promotes lipolysis and gluconeogenesis in muscles. Prolactin production is increased during pregnancy and breast-feeding and reduced by dopamine.

Reference: Hypothalamic and pituitary function. *Anaesthesia and Intensive Care Medicine* 2005; 6: 324–5.

### 3.103 Regarding endocrine physiology:

☐ A When testing random cortisol levels, a normal result in the evening may be one-quarter of the normal morning level

☐ B In the absence of adrenocorticotrophic hormone (ACTH), the zona glomerulosa of the adrenals is most affected

☐ C Exogenous steroids are administered to steroid-dependent patients perioperatively, as they have functional atrophy of their hypothalamic–pituitary axis

☐ D Pain is a stimulus for ADH release

☐ E Oxytocin has no antidiuretic properties

### 3.104 Regarding adrenal physiology:

☐ A Cholesterol is the precursor of all corticosteroids

☐ B The zona glomerulosa secretes glucocorticoids

☐ C Aldosterone prevents excess sodium secretion in sweat

☐ D Serum potassium concentration is the most important stimulus for aldosterone release

☐ E The zona glomerulosa lacks 17α-hydroxylase

## 3.103 Answers:

- A True
- B False
- C True
- D True
- E False

Normal morning levels of cortisol are ~20 µg/dl. Evening levels fall to ~5 µg/dl. The adrenal glands atrophy without ACTH stimulation but the zona glomerulosa is least affected and continues to secrete aldosterone and maintain electrolyte balance. The concern with steroid-dependent patients is that they may suffer a hypotensive event during this stressful period. ADH release is increased by increased osmolality, hypovolaemia, hypotension, pain, hyperthermia and stress. The normal role of oxytocin is that of uterine contraction and contraction of breast tissue to release milk. It has some antidiuretic activity but only at most 1% that of ADH.

## 3.104 Answers:

- A True
- B False
- C True
- D True
- E True

Corticosteroids refer to both glucocorticoids and mineralocorticoids. The adrenals are divided into three zones of different cells. The zona glomerulosa secretes mineralocorticoids, the zona fasciculata secretes glucocorticoids and the zona reticularis secretes cortisol and androgens. Aldosterone affects sweat glands and salivary glands, reducing sodium loss and increasing potassium secretion. Even small increases in serum potassium can hugely increase the release of aldosterone. The renin–angiotensin axis is also a stimulator for its release. The zona glomerulosa is unable to synthesis cortisol as it lacks 17α-hydroxylase.

### 3.105  Cortisol:

- ☐ A  Increases gluconeogenesis
- ☐ B  Increases migration of leukocytes into inflamed areas
- ☐ C  Decreases the number of circulating eosinophils
- ☐ D  Binds to nuclei resulting in production of mRNA
- ☐ E  May remain elevated for 72 hours postoperatively

### 3.106  Regarding the adrenal medulla:

- ☐ A  It is supplied by postganglionic cholinergic fibres
- ☐ B  Most of the norepinephrine formed is converted to epinephrine
- ☐ C  Epinephrine synthesis is stimulated by cortisol
- ☐ D  Upon stimulation, the adrenal medulla releases catecholamines by exocytosis of vesicles
- ☐ E  The plasma half-life of epinephrine is longer than that of norepinephrine

### 3.105 Answers:

- A True
- B False
- C True
- D True
- E True

The actions of cortisol include increasing gluconeogenesis, protein catabolism, fatty acid mobilisation and anti-inflammatory effects. These anti-inflammatory effects include stabilisation of lysosomal membranes, a reduction in migration of leukocytes into inflamed tissues, a reduction of circulating eosinophils and decreased capillary permeability. Cortisol attenuates the complement system and the formation of mediators of inflammation from the arachidonic pathway (decreases phospholipase $A_2$ production) but does not directly affect antibody–antigen reaction or histamine release. In response to surgery, the cortisol level rises because of hypothalamic stimulation from injured tissue and proinflammatory mediators directly activating the adrenals. The levels normally return to normal within 24 hours; however, can remain elevated for longer depending on the extent of the surgery.

### 3.106 Answers:

- A False
- B True
- C True
- D True
- E False

Norepinephrine is converted to epinephrine by phenylethanolamine-*N*-methyl transferase. Cortisol passes via intra-adrenal portal vessels to increase the activity of this enzyme, so increasing the synthesis and release of epinephrine. Stimulation of the adrenal medulla by release of acetylcholine from preganglionic cholinergic fibres causes an increase in calcium entry; this causes exocytosis of vesicles containing the catecholamines. The plasma half-life of epinephrine is 10–15 seconds compared to that of norepinephrine at 20–30 seconds.

**3.107 Regarding haemoglobinopathies:**

☐ A  A haemophilia A carrier with a baseline factor VIII activity level of 60% is at risk of bleeding

☐ B  Sickle cell anaemia is inherited in an autosomal dominant fashion

☐ C  β-Thalassemia major results in reduced amounts of HbA

☐ D  β-Thalassemia major is inherited in an X-linked recessive fashion

☐ E  Patients suffering with HbH disease have only one functioning α globin

**3.108 Regarding pancreatic function:**

☐ A  There are twice as many α cells as there are β cells in the pancreas

☐ B  Approximately 1.5 l of pancreatic secretions are produced per day

☐ C  Infection decreases the release of glucagon

☐ D  Glucagon acts via tyrosine kinase

☐ E  The islet cells drain into the portal vein

**3.107 Answers:**

- A False
- B False
- C True
- D False
- E True

A total of 35% activity level for factor VIII is the cut-off for the likelihood of bleeding and, even then, this is unlikely. Sickle cell anaemia is inherited in an autosomal recessive fashion. β-Thalassemia major causes reduced synthesis of the β-globin chain. This leads to a microcytic, hypochromic anaemia with reduced HbA. Its inheritance is autosomal recessive. HbBarts results in death *in utero* or during the neonatal period. It results from having no α-globin gene.

Reference: *Inherited Haematological Conditions.* Education Forum. Doctors.net.uk.

**3.108 Answers:**

- A False
- B True
- C False
- D False
- E True

Only 1–2% of the pancreatic mass is attributed to the islets of Langerhans. They are made up of ~25% α cells that produce glucagon, ~75% β cells that produce insulin, ~5% δ cells that produce somatostatin and ~5% F cells that produce pancreatic polypeptide. Glucagon is released in response to hypoglycaemia, amino acids, sepsis, trauma, β-adrenergic agonists, glucocorticoids and theophylline. Glucagons act via Gs-protein coupled receptors causing activation of adenylyl cyclase and producing cAMP. Insulin acts via tyrosine kinase.

**3.109 Insulin:**

☐ A  Is stored in the pancreas complexed with zinc

☐ B  Has a plasma half-life of 5 minutes

☐ C  Release is increased by the hormone somatostatin

☐ D  Release occurs because of voltage-dependent calcium-channel opening

☐ E  Valine is dependent on insulin for its cellular uptake

**3.109 Answers:**

- A True
- B True
- C False
- D True
- E True

Insulin release is increased by carbohydrates, amino acids, hormones (glucagon, gastric inhibitory peptide, gastrin, secretin, cholecystokinin) and neural factors.

Insulin is stored in β cells complexed with zinc. Depolarisation of the β-cell membrane, by blocking potassium channels, causes influx of calcium that causes insulin vesicles to fuse with the membrane. Certain amino acids are dependent on insulin for their cellular uptake, including valine, leucine, tyrosine and phenylalanine.

**3.110   Effects of insulin include increased:**

☐   A   Gluconeogenesis

☐   B   Cell membrane permeability to sodium

☐   C   Glycolysis in muscle

☐   D   Lipoprotein lipase activity

☐   E   Esterification of fatty acids

## 3.110 Answers:

- A False
- B False
- C True
- D True
- E True

Lipoprotein lipase activity increases; this causes the breakdown of triglycerides into fatty acids, so facilitating their storage in fat cells. Hormone-sensitive lipases are inhibited, reducing triglyceride breakdown within fat cells.

The table demonstrates the effects of insulin.

| Substrate | Increases | Decreases |
|---|---|---|
| Carbohydrate | Glycogenolysis | Glycogen synthesis |
| | Glycolysis | Gluconeogenesis |
| Protein | Amino acid uptake and oxidation | Protein breakdown |
| | Protein synthesis | |
| Fat | Fatty acid and $\alpha$-glycerophosphate synthesis | Ketogenesis |
| | Lipoprotein lipase | Hormone-sensitive lipase |
| | | Triglyceride breakdown |

**3.111 Regarding the lower oesophageal sphincter (LOS):**

- ☐ A The mechanism of its action consists of both smooth muscle and skeletal muscle
- ☐ B Its neurogenic tone is influenced by vagal innervation
- ☐ C LOS pressure minus intragastric pressure gives a gastric barrier pressure
- ☐ D LOS pressure is increased by cricoid pressure
- ☐ E LOS pressure gradually decreases during pregnancy

**3.111 Answers:**

- A True
- B True
- C True
- D False
- E True

The LOS is formed by smooth muscle at the lowest 2–4 cm of the oesophagus. The mechanism for its action also involves skeletal muscle from the diaphragm. Muscle tone is multifactorial, neurogenic and myogenic. Normal LOS pressure is 10–30 mmHg. Gastric barrier pressure is LOS pressure minus intragastric pressure. LOS pressure may decrease with cricoid pressure secondary to the stimulation of afferent mechanoreceptors in the pharynx.

| Increased LOS tone | Decreased LOS tone |
| --- | --- |
| Gastrin | Cricoid pressure |
| Modulin | Alcohol |
| α-Adrenergic stimulation | β-Adrenergic stimulation |
| Metoclopramide | Opiates |
| Histamine | Secretin |
| Anticholinesterase | Glucagon |
| Increased intragastric pressure | Gastric inhibitory peptide |
| Suxamethonium | Bilateral vagotomy |

**3.112   During exercise:**

☐ A   ATP stored within the muscle can supply the energy required for the first 1 minute of vigorous exercise

☐ B   Approximately one-fifth of the lactate released due to anaerobic metabolism is utilised by the heart

☐ C   Anaerobic metabolism in the tissues releases three ATP molecules per six-carbon unit of carbohydrate

☐ D   There is a leftward shift of the oxyhaemoglobin dissociation curve

☐ E   Oxygen deficit in muscles occurs as anaerobic metabolism supports energy demands before enhanced oxygen uptake

**3.112 Answers:**

- A  False
- B  True
- C  True
- D  False
- E  True

The ATP stores within muscle are limited and can supply enough energy for only 1–2 seconds of vigorous exercise. After this time, ATP is supplied by aerobic and anaerobic metabolism. Anaerobic metabolism can produce a rapid energy source but with limited amounts, whereas aerobic metabolism can produce large amounts at slower rates. Most of the lactate is converted to glycogen in the liver, although cardiac muscle uses some. Regarding option C, aerobic metabolism of a similar CHO molecule yields 38 ATP molecules. (Two ATP molecules are yielded from the breakdown of glucose to pyruvate and a further 36 ATP molecules are produced from the breakdown of pyruvate in the tricarboxylic acid cycle.) With increases in $H^+$, $CO_2$ and temperature, the curve shifts to the right. Oxygen debt is paid back at the end of exercise, ie the oxygen consumption remains high despite exercise cessation.

Reference: Physiological effects of exercise. *Continuing Education in Anaesthesia, Critical Care and Pain* 2004; 4(6): 185–8.

**3.113  The following are correct regarding type I muscle fibres when compared with type II muscle fibres:**

&#9633;  A  They are fast acting

&#9633;  B  They have a high mitochondrial content

&#9633;  C  They have a high myoglobin content

&#9633;  D  Their main energy supply is anaerobic

&#9633;  E  Their time to peak tension is approximately twice as fast

### 3.113 Answers:

- A False
- B True
- C True
- D False
- E False

Type I muscle fibres are slow twitch fibres. They are more numerous in the muscles involved in posture and are well suited for prolonged activities and activities of low intensity. They rely on aerobic metabolism and contain a high content of both myoglobin and mitochondria. Their time to peak tension is ~110 ms compared with 50 ms for type II muscle fibres. Type II muscle fibres are fast twitch. They are recruited for fast acting and forceful exercise. They rely on rapid anaerobic metabolism, and appear white in colour, containing low numbers of mitochondria and myoglobin.

Reference: Physiological effects of exercise. *Continuing Education in Anaesthesia, Critical Care and Pain* 2004; 4(6): 185–8.

**3.114  The physiology of exercise:**

☐  A  Breathing capacity limits oxygen delivery to tissues at maximum exertion

☐  B  As lactic acid increases $PaCO_2$ decreases to normalise pH

☐  C  The initial increase in ventilation can be attributed to the changes in $PaO_2$ and $PaCO_2$

☐  D  Trained athletes do not have such an increase in heart rate at maximum exercise when compared with non-trained athletes

☐  E  Blood pressure increases during exercise

**3.114 Answers:**

- A False
- B True
- C False
- D True
- E True

Breathing capacity does not limit oxygen delivery in normal individuals even during maximum exercise, and haemoglobin saturation remains unaffected, ie fully saturated. As lactic acid increases because of anaerobic metabolism in the tissues, $PaCO_2$ decreases to maintain pH. There is a rapid increase in ventilation at the start of exercise. This is thought to be because of motor and proprioceptive input from the exercising muscles and joints. Peripheral and central chemoreceptors, temperature changes, brain-stem and respiratory centre activity all seem to have a part to play in increasing ventilation. Trained athletes increase their stroke volume largely to result in a lower heart rate than non-trained athletes. Blood pressure increases slightly with a rise in cardiac output. This rise is attenuated by the decrease in peripheral vascular resistance by vasodilatation.

Reference: Physiological effects of exercise. *Continuing Education in Anaesthesia, Critical Care and Pain* 2004; 4(6): 185–8.

**3.115** $VO_{2max}$:

- [ ] A  Refers to the maximum oxygen delivery
- [ ] B  Can be reduced when at altitude secondary to pulmonary limitations
- [ ] C  During maximum exercise is most affected by increased blood flow
- [ ] D  Is increased with the use of erythropoietin
- [ ] E  Is doubled if mitochondria are doubled

**3.115  Answers:**

- A  False
- B  True
- C  True
- D  True
- E  False

$VO_{2max}$ = cardiac output × (arterial oxygen content - mixed venous oxygen content).

It refers to maximal oxygen uptake. Normal subjects exercising at sea level will have $VO_{2max}$ limited by delivery of oxygen to the muscles. The uptake of oxygen by the muscles is not the limiting factor. It may be intuitive that doubling the mitochondria would double the oxygen uptake; however, this has not been shown to be the limiting step. Increasing capillary density increases the time and volume of blood within the muscle; this increases oxygen extraction. Arterial oxygen content is altered by altitude and erythropoietin so altering $VO_{2max}$.

Reference: Physiological effects of exercise. *Continuing Education in Anaesthesia, Critical Care and Pain* 2004; 4(6): 185–8.

**3.116 Regarding the physiology of sleep:**

&#9633; A   Rapid eye movement (REM) sleep decreases with age

&#9633; B   Facts learned just before sleep are poorly remembered when compared with facts learned earlier in the day

&#9633; C   REM sleep is associated with limb twitching

&#9633; D   Hyperpolarisation of $\alpha$-motor neurons during REM sleep prevent individuals acting out their dreams

&#9633; E   There is an increase in ADH secretion

**3.116  Answers:**

- A  True
- B  True
- C  True
- D  True
- E  True

Neonates experience ~50% REM sleep; this falls to ~25% in 2 year olds. A normal adult experiences ~15–20% REM sleep. As age increases REM sleep decreases and sleep becomes more fragmented. REM sleep is characterised by eye movements and a characteristic EEG of mixed frequency, low-voltage and saw-tooth waves. It has two phases: tonic and phasic. Tonic REM sleep is associated with a reduction in muscle activity. Phasic REM sleep is associated with muscle movement and twitching. Option D refers to the atonia of REM sleep causing relaxation of skeletal muscles. Waking during this stage of sleep can occur and is alarming although not harmful. The muscles of respiration and upper airway tone are preserved.

Reference: Physiology of sleep. *British Journal of Anaesthesia CEPD Reviews* 2003; 3(3): 69–74.

**3.117  The following is correct regarding sleep:**

- ☐ A  Thermoregulation is inhibited during sleep
- ☐ B  Melatonin secretion occurs usually at dawn
- ☐ C  γ-Aminobutyric acid (GABA) secretion is associated with slow-wave sleep induction
- ☐ D  The first night after anaesthesia, the patient will have more REM sleep than normal
- ☐ E  Nights 2–5 postoperatively are important for recovery of a normal sleep pattern

**3.118  Platelets:**

- ☐ A  Take 10 days to be produced in the bone marrow
- ☐ B  Are cell membranes surrounding megakaryocyte cytoplasm
- ☐ C  Are nucleated
- ☐ D  Express HLA antigen but not the ABO antigens
- ☐ E  Have glycoproteins GPIIb/GPIIIa that bind to von Willebrand's factor (vWF)

## 3.117 Answers:

- A False
- B False
- C True
- D False
- E True

Thermoregulation is preserved with sleep, although the threshold for shivering is reduced and core temperature is reduced by some 0.5°C. Melatonin is secreted from the pineal gland in response to onset of darkness. Is thought to allow the onset of sleep without being hypnotic. It is available over the counter in the USA but is currently available only by prescription in the UK. The first postoperative night is thought to contain little or no REM sleep which may be because of the surgical insult or medications. Nights 2–5 are important for recovery of this lost sleep.

Reference: Physiology of sleep. *British Journal of Anaesthesia CEPD Reviews* 2003; 3(3): 69–74.

## 3.118 Answers:

- A True
- B True
- C False
- D False
- E True

Bone marrow stem cells develop into megakaryocytes, which undergo non-mitotic nuclear replication. Platelets bud off the surface of these enlarged megakaryocytes. This process takes 10 days. Platelets express both ABO and HLA class I antigens.

Platelets lack a nucleus and are unable to manufacture their own proteins. They have a number of glycoproteins on their external coat including GPIa, which binds collagen, and GPIIb/GPIIIa, which bind vWF and fibronectin.

### 3.119  The following increase platelet aggregation:

☐ A  Thromboxane $A_2$

☐ B  Prostacyclin

☐ C  Released ADP

☐ D  Fibrinogen

☐ E  Von Willebrand's factor

### 3.120  Regarding coagulation:

☐ A  The initial activation of the plasma factor XII is calcium dependent

☐ B  In vitro, kallikrein release reduces the activation of factor XII

☐ C  Factor XI is found on the surface of platelets

☐ D  Activation of factor X occurs in the presence of factor V

☐ E  In vivo, activated factor VII seems largely to activate factor IX rather than factor X

### 3.119 Answers:

- A True
- B False
- C True
- D True
- E True

Thromboxane synthetase is released when platelets contact damaged endothelium. The released thromboxane causes an increase in ADP levels and platelet aggregation. The ADP binds and activates the GPIIb/GPIIIa complex. Aggregation leads to more ADP release, ie positive feedback. Prostacyclin, in the vascular endothelium, stimulates platelet cAMP production, which decreases ADP release and reduces aggregation. The release of fibrinogen and vWF from α-granules enhances platelet adhesion and aggregation.

### 3.120 Answers:

- A False
- B False
- C True
- D False
- E True

Initial activation of factor XII is calcium independent. It is caused by the interaction of factor XII with negatively charged surfaces on collagen or glass in vivo. Kallikrein activates the coagulation cascade (as used in the thromboelastogram).

Factor XI is found on subendothelial tissue and on platelet surfaces. Plasma concentrations are ~5 μg/ml. Factor X activation occurs in the presence of activated factor IX, factor VIII, calcium and platelet phospholipids (including phospholipid $PF_3$).

Reference: Haemostasis, blood platelets and coagulation. *Anaesthesia and Intensive Care Medicine* 2004; 5: 189–91.

### 3.121 The complement system:

☐ A The classic pathway is initiated by antigen–antibody complexes

☐ B All antibodies are capable of activating complement

☐ C Cell-bound C3b facilitates T- and B-cell activation

☐ D Radiological media can activate the alternative complement pathway

☐ E The final common pathway results in bacterial cell membrane lysis

## 3.121 Answers:

- A True
- B False
- C True
- D True
- E True

The complement system describes a series of proteins (mostly hepatically synthesised) that are involved in inflammation, autoimmune disorders and host defence. The classic pathway involves the activation of C1 by antigen–antibody complexes. Only IgM and IgG are able to activate the classic pathway. Once activated, C4 and C2 are cleaved and activate C3, which in turn activates C5. C3a fragments cause vascular leakage and histamine release. Damaged cells, pathogens, foreign material or IgA accelerates the spontaneous cleavage of C3, giving rise to the alternative pathway. The final common pathway is the membrane attack pathway, producing C5b–9 complex. This causes non-receptor-mediated cell activation and cytotoxicity. The complement system is complex. This is only a brief overview.

**3.122 The following can be expected in an area affected by complex regional pain syndrome (CRPS) type 2:**

☐ A  Nail changes

☐ B  Hot skin

☐ C  Abnormal sweating

☐ D  Osteomalacia

☐ E  Actual nerve injury

**3.122  Answers:**

- A  True
- B  False
- C  True
- D  False
- E  True

Complex regional pain syndromes are associated with sympathetic dysfunction.

Type 1 consists of pain in an extremity that does not correspond to the distribution of a single peripheral nerve whereas, in type 2, the pain is normally in the distribution of a damaged nerve (ie there is actual nerve injury). Sympathetic dysfunction leads to sensory, vascular, oedema/sweating and motor/trophic abnormalities (including nail changes and osteoporosis). The area affected classically feels cold and clammy.

Vitamin D deficiency in adults gives rise to osteomalacia.

The reference below includes the revised diagnostic criteria for CRPS.

Reference: Complex regional pain syndrome. *Continuing Education in Anaesthesia, Critical Care and Pain* 2007; 7(2): 51–4.

**3.123   Regarding CRPS:**

☐  A   Type II results from peripheral nervous system activity after a partial nerve injury

☐  B   Nociceptor activity increases in response to prostaglandin release

☐  C   Increased circulating cytokines may be detected in the early phase

☐  D   The peripheral nervous system is responsible for the long-term changes seen

☐  E   NMDA (*N*-methyl-D-aspartate)-receptor enhancement may have a role to play

**3.123  Answers:**

- A  True
- B  True
- C  True
- D  False
- E  True

The pathogenesis of CRPS is still not certain. $\alpha_2$-Receptors (Gi-coupled receptors, widespread throughout the nervous system) become sensitised in the nociceptor C-fibres such that they are more sensitive to the circulating and local (from postganglionic sympathetic fibres) norepinephrine. Norepinephrine also induces the release of prostaglandins that increases the nociceptor activity. During the initial inflammatory phase cytokine levels increase. Although the initial response may be peripherally mediated, the wind-up of the CNS is responsible for the disabling symptoms.

Reference: Complex regional pain syndrome. *Continuing Education in Anaesthesia, Critical Care and Pain* 2007; 7(2): 51–4.

**3.124   Regarding the ascending and descending tracts of the spinal cord:**

☐  A   The fasciculus gracilis conveys proprioception sensation from the upper body

☐  B   The lateral spinothalamic tract transmits pain and temperature sensation

☐  C   The anterior spinothalamic tracts cross at the levels of innervation

☐  D   Lateral corticospinal tracts decussate in the medulla

☐  E   Proprioception is conveyed to the cerebellum via the spinocerebellar tracts

## 3.124 Answers:

- A  False
- B  True
- C  False
- D  True
- E  True

Of the ascending pathways, the posterior column is divided into the fasciculus gracilis and cuneatus. These ascend in the dorsal column to reach their respective nuclei. They decussate in the medulla. The fasciculus gracilis carries touch, vibration and proprioception from the lower body, whereas the fasciculus cuneatus carries these senses from the upper body. The spinothalamic tracts enter the cord and decussate to ascend on the contralateral side. The lateral spinothalamic tract conveys pain and temperature whereas the anterior spinothalamic tract conveys touch and pressure. Of the descending pathways, the lateral corticospinal tracts decussate in the medulla and descend in the spinal cord. It conveys motor innervation from the cerebral cortex. The anterior corticospinal tract does not decussate until reaching the distal anterior horn cells.

**3.125 Left-sided partial transection of the spinal cord at T10 leads to the following clinical symptoms:**

- ☐ A No straight-leg raise of the right leg
- ☐ B No pain sensation in the left greater toe
- ☐ C Absent left knee reflex
- ☐ D Anal sphincter impairment
- ☐ E Loss of vibration sense in the left foot

**3.126 Positive pressure ventilation increases:**

- ☐ A ADH release
- ☐ B Dead space
- ☐ C Left ventricular compliance
- ☐ D Renin–angiotensin system suppression
- ☐ E Cerebral perfusion pressure

**3.125 Answers:**

- A True
- B False
- C False
- D False
- E True

Hemisection of the spinal cord, or Brown–Séquard syndrome, affects both ascending and descending tracts, so knowledge of both is required: see Question 3.37.

It would result in ipsilateral loss of vibration and proprioception, contralateral loss of pain and temperature, and ipsilateral paralysis. A brisk knee reflex (L3–4) would be expected with a T10 lesion as it would act as an upper motor neuron lesion.

**3.126 Answers:**

- A True
- B True
- C False
- D False
- E False

Raised intrathoracic pressure caused by positive pressure during inspiration decreases cardiac output by decreasing venous return, mild cardiac tamponade and increased PVR. Left ventricular compliance reduces secondary to lung expansion and bulging of the right ventricle against an increased PVR. Dead space increases with the introduction of tubing and airway devices. The decreases in cardiac output decrease renal blood flow and increase activation of the renin–angiotensin system. Cerebral perfusion pressure falls as the mean arterial pressure (MAP) is lower and the cardiovascular performance (CVP) higher with intermittent positive pressure ventilation (IPPV).

### 3.127 Magnesium:

☐ A  Increases end-plate sensitivity to acetylcholine
☐ B  Is a predominantly intracellular ion
☐ C  Activates membrane pumps in cells that transport calcium outside the cell
☐ D  Is an NMDA-receptor agonist
☐ E  Deficiency resembles digitalis toxicity on the ECG

### 3.128 Regarding CNS physiology:

☐ A  A-waves on an intracranial pressure (ICP) monitoring trace are associated with raised ICP
☐ B  Brain tissue accounts for 50% of the total fixed brain volume
☐ C  A rising ICP initially triggers changes in CSF distribution
☐ D  Cerebral blood flow autoregulation occurs at an MAP range of 50–150 mmHg
☐ E  Cerebral blood flow starts to rise only once $PaO_2$ falls below 10 kPa

**3.127   Answers:**

- A  True
- B  True
- C  True
- D  False
- E  True

Magnesium is the second most prevalent intracellular cation after potassium. Half of all magnesium is present in bone, 20% is in muscle, 30% is protein bound and only 1% is extracellular. It is the natural calcium antagonist, increasing its expulsion from cells and preventing its intracellular access by acting as a competitor for transmembrane channels. Magnesium is an NMDA-receptor antagonist and is being investigated for pain therapies.

**3.128   Answers:**

- A  True
- B  False
- C  True
- D  True
- E  False

ICP monitoring demonstrates A-, B- and C-waves. B- and C-waves are affected by the normal pressure changes associated with variations in respiration and blood pressure. A-waves are associated with raised ICP; they are also known as plateau waves. The skull is a fixed volume containing $\sim$85% brain tissue, $\sim$10% cranial CSF and $\sim$5% cerebral blood. With a rising ICP, the first compensatory mechanism is the change in distribution of CSF to the spinal space and an increase in CSF reabsorption. Limited changes in the volume of the other compartments occur. Cerebral blood flow increases linearly, 2–4% for every 0.13 kPa increase in $P_aCO_2$ (between 2.7 and 10.7 kPa). Note that severe hypotension can abolish arteriole responses to $P_aCO_2$. Cerebral blood flow rises when $P_aO_2$ falls below 6.7 kPa.

**3.129   Regarding scoring systems:**

☐  A  An Ashwell shape chart is a score of waist to height ratio (in centimetres)

☐  B  A body mass index (BMI) of 27 is described as being normal

☐  C  An APACHE II score uses 20 physiological measurements in the acute physiology score

☐  D  The maximum points awardable on an apgar score is 10

☐  E  Flexing in response to pain earns two points on a Glasgow Coma Scale (GCS) score

**3.130   The following blood tests are within the normal range:**

☐  A  Ionised calcium 1.2 mmol/l

☐  B  Magnesium 0.85 mmol/l

☐  C  Glycated haemoglobin 5%

☐  D  Mean red cell volume 98 fl

☐  E  Chloride 82 mmol/l

## 3.129 Answers:

- A True
- B False
- C False
- D True
- E False

A score of 41–50 on an Ashwell shape chart is desirable, with a score of 51–60 caution is recommended and with a score of over 60 action is required.

BMI is weight (kg)/height (m$^2$). A score of 18.5–24.9 is considered normal, 25–29.9 is overweight and >30 is obese.

APACHE II or acute physiology and chronic health evaluation version II uses 12 physiological measurements in the acute physiology score. It also takes into account age and chronic health points, yielding a maximum score of 71.

Apgar scoring assesses heart rate, respiratory effort, muscle tone, irritability and colour, giving a maximum score of 10. Flexing in response to pain is awarded a score of three points on the GCS.

## 3.130 Answers:

- A True
- B True
- C True
- D False
- E False

The following are the correct ranges:

- ionised calcium              1.0–1.25 mmol/l
- magnesium                   0.75–1.05 mmol/l
- glycated haemoglobin (HbAlc)  5–8%
- mean red cell volume        76–96 fl
- chloride                    95–105 mmol/l.

Reference: Longmore M, Wilkinson IB *et al. Oxford Handbook of Clinical Medicine*. 3rd edn. Oxford Unviersity Press, 2004.

**3.131   Regarding phaeochromocytomas:**

☐  A  10% occur outside the adrenal medulla

☐  B  They are tumours of chromaffin cells

☐  C  Up to 50% of in-patient hospital deaths from this condition
          occur during anaesthesia

☐  D  Epinephrine secreting tumours present with sustained
          hypertension

☐  E  The most sensitive test for diagnosis is elevated urinary
          vanillylmandelic acid (VMA)

**3.131 Answers:**

- A True
- B True
- C True
- D False
- E False

Phaeochromocytomas are the disorder of 10 per cent: 10% are extra-adrenal, 10% are bilateral and 10% are metastatic. A total of 25–50% of deaths in hospital occur during anaesthesia; ~80% of phaeochromocytomas will secrete norepinephrine. The presentation will be that of sustained hypertension, headache and palpitations. Epinephrine-secreting tumours will present with paroxysmal symptoms including sweating, anxiety and tremor. Although urinary VMA is tested for, it is a less sensitive diagnostic tool than testing for elevated plasma and urinary catecholamines.

Reference: Recognition and management of phaeochromocytoma. *Anaesthesia and Intensive Care Medicine* 2005; 6: 336–40.

# Anatomy

# MCQs

*Indicate your answers with a tick or cross in the boxes provided.*

### 3.132 Regarding vertebrae:

☐ A  A typical cervical vertebra has a bifid spinous process

☐ B  The body of the first cervical vertebra is small to allow articulation with C2

☐ C  The dens of C2 is held in position by the transverse ligament of the C1

☐ D  The transverse processes of the thoracic vertebrae articulate with the ribs

☐ E  The spine consists of 25 true vertebrae

Anatomy MCQs

### 3.132  Answers:

- A  True
- B  False
- C  True
- D  True
- E  False

There are 24 true vertebrae, 7 cervical, 12 thoracic and 5 lumbar. False vertebrae refer to the fused sacral and vestigial coccyx.

Bifid cervical spinous processes allow connection of the neck extensors. C1, the atlas, lacks both body and spine as it articulates with C2, allowing free movement of the head. The dens of C2 is a projection from its superior surface that articulates with the anterior arch of C1. Both the transverse processes and bodies of the thoracic vertebrae have facets with which to articulate with the ribs.

Reference: Cervical, thoracic and lumbar vertebrae. *Anaesthesia and Intensive Care Medicine* 2003; 3: 434–6.

**3.133  Regarding spinal nerves and dermatomes:**

☐  A  All cervical spinal nerves leave the cord above their associated cervical vertebrae

☐  B  The posterior nerve root carries sensory fibres from the skin

☐  C  The anterior nerve roots carry motor fibres to the skeletal muscle

☐  D  Cell bodies contributing to the posterior nerve roots lie within the anterior grey horns of the spinal cord

☐  E  The posterior primary rami supply only sensory innervation

## 3.133 Answers:

- A False
- B True
- C True
- D False
- E False

There are 31 pairs of spinal nerves. There are eight cervical nerves. Cervical nerves I–VII leave the spinal cord above their respective vertebra via the intervertebral foramen. The eighth cervical and subsequent spinal nerves leave below their associated vertebra. The anterior roots are motor and autonomic and have cell bodies within the anterior grey horns of the spinal cord. The posterior nerve roots are sensory and have their cell bodies in the posterior root ganglion, which lies outside the cord. The anterior and posterior nerve roots fuse.

Having fused they then divide into anterior and posterior primary rami. The anterior primary rami provide motor and sensory innervation to the limbs and front and sides of the neck, thorax and abdomen. The posterior primary rami provide sensory and motor innervation to the back with a few exceptions, eg the first cervical posterior ramus is only motor.

Reference: Spinal nerves and dermatomes. *Anaesthesia and Intensive Care Medicine* 2004; 5: 150–1.

**3.134** **The following nerves are correctly matched with the foramen through which they exit the skull:**

☐ A  The internal acoustic meatus transmits the facial nerve

☐ B  The foramen ovale transmits the maxillary division of the trigeminal nerve

☐ C  The superior orbital fissure transmits both the superior and inferior branches of the oculomotor nerve

☐ D  The hypoglossal nerve exits the skull with the vagus nerve

☐ E  All the nerves controlling movements of the globe of the eye exit the skull via the superior orbital fissure

**3.135** **Regarding interpretation of cervical spine radiographs:**

☐ A  Adequacy of film requires visualisation from the lower clivus to the upper body of C7 vertebra

☐ B  The distance between the odontoid and the axis is accepted as normal if it measures 2 mm

☐ C  An open-mouth view is used to assess the odontoid process

☐ D  The spinal cord lies in the canal between the posterior vertebral and spinolaminar lines

☐ E  Above the larynx, acceptable soft tissue thickness is less than one-half of the vertebral body width

**3.134 Answers:**

- A True
- B False
- C True
- D False
- E True

The internal acoustic meatus transmits the facial and the vestibulocochlear nerves. The foramen ovale transmits the mandibular division of the trigeminal nerve. The maxillary division is transmitted by the foramen rotundum. The jugular foramen transmits the glossopharyngeal, vagus and accessory nerve. The superior orbital fissure transmits a number of structures including the following nerves: lacrimal, frontal, trochlear, oculomotor, nasociliary and abducens. It also transmits the superior ophthalmic vein.

Reference: Andreas Erdmann. *Concise Anatomy for Anaesthetists*. Cambridge University Press, 2001.

**3.135 Answers:**

- A False
- B True
- C True
- D True
- E False

Adequacy of film requires visualisation from the base of the skull (clivus) to the upper body of T1. Open-mouth odontoid views enable visualisation of C1 and C2. There are four lines that must be assessed for alignment when reviewing a cervical spine radiograph: the anterior vertebral line, the posterior vertebral line (which forms the anterior wall of the spinal canal) , the facet line and the spinolaminar line (which forms the posterior wall of the spinal canal).

Acceptable soft tissue distances are less than one-third of the vertebral body width above the larynx and not more than one vertebral body width below the larynx: 2 mm is the normal odontoid, axis distance but up to 5 mm is accepted.

Reference: Advance Life Support Group, *Advanced Paediatric Life Support: The Practical Approach*. 4th edn, 2004.

### 3.136  The stellate ganglion:

- ☐ A  Is the ganglion through which all sympathetic efferents to the head, neck and arm pass
- ☐ B  Is present in all patients
- ☐ C  Lies behind the vertebral artery
- ☐ D  Blockade may help alleviate Raynaud's syndrome
- ☐ E  Blockade is performed lateral to the carotid sheath

### 3.137  Chest radiograph interpretation:

- ☐ A  In a posteroanterior (PA) film, the normal heart shadow is <50% of the thoracic diameter
- ☐ B  On a lateral radiograph, the mitral valve lies above the line from the anterior costophrenic angle to the hilum
- ☐ C  The left hilar lies 3–4 cm above the right
- ☐ D  The left hemi-diaphragm is usually 2 cm below the right
- ☐ E  In left lower lobe collapse, the left heart border is lost

**3.136  Answers:**

- A  True
- B  False
- C  True
- D  True
- E  False

This ganglion represents the fused inferior cervical and first thoracic sympathetic ganglion. It is present in 80% of patients. Sympathetic blockade results in vasodilatation, which alleviates Raynaud's syndrome. To perform the block, the patient is usually supine, once the transverse process of C7 is detected; the needle is inserted medial to the carotid sheath, which is retracted laterally to avoid injury.

**3.137  Answers:**

- A  True
- B  False
- C  False
- D  True
- E  False

Option B describes the normal position of the aortic value; the mitral valve lies below this line. The left hilar normally lies 1–2 cm higher than the right. The left hemi-diaphragm is usually ~2 cm lower than the right, the right being higher because of the liver. Collapse of the left lower lobe gives rise to the sail sign with a triangle of increased opacity behind the heart. The left heart border is preserved.

Reference: *Anaesthesia and Intensive Care A–Z*. Third edition. S. Yentis.

**3.138 Regarding cerebral anatomy:**

☐ A A total of 80% of the arterial blood supply is supplied by the internal carotid artery

☐ B The circle of Willis is the anastomosis of the carotid and vertebral arterial supplies

☐ C The posterior cerebral artery supplies the occipital lobe

☐ D The anterior cerebral artery supplies the lateral part of the cerebral hemisphere

☐ E The superior cerebellar artery is most commonly a branch of the vertebral artery

**3.139 Coronary circulation:**

☐ A In 90% of individuals the right coronary artery is dominant

☐ B The left coronary artery carries six-sevenths of the coronary blood flow

☐ C Blood flow to the left ventricle in the epicardial and sub-epicardial vessels ceases during systole

☐ D Normal resting coronary blood flow is 250 ml/min

☐ E Most venous blood from the coronary circulation drains into the right atrium via the thebesian veins

**3.138 Answers:**

- A False
- B True
- C True
- D False
- E False

Two-thirds of the cerebral blood supply is from the internal carotid artery. One-third is supplied by the vertebral arteries.

The anterior cerebral artery supplies superior and medial parts of the cerebral hemisphere.

The middle cerebral artery supplies most of the lateral side of the hemisphere.

The posterior cerebral artery supplies the occipital lobe and medial side of the temporal lobe.

The superior cerebellar and anterior inferior cerebellar arteries are branches of the basilar artery formed from vertebral and anterior spinal arteries.

Reference: Yentis SM, Hirsch NP and Smith GB. *Anaesthesia and intensive care A–Z*. An encyclopaedia of principles and practice. 3rd edn. Butterworth Heinemann 2004.

**3.139 Answers:**

- A False
- B True
- C False
- D True
- E False

The right coronary artery is thought to be dominant in 50% of patients.

Epicardial and subepicardial vessels are largely unaffected by extravascular systemic pressure; however, subendocardial vessels of the left ventricle are compressed during systole.

Most venous blood drains via the coronary sinus into the right atrium.

The thebesian veins drain venous blood directly into left ventricle.

**3.140 Regarding coronary nervous innervation:**

☐ A Both parasympathetic and sympathetic nervous systems innervating the heart originate in the medulla

☐ B The right vagus acts mainly on the atrioventricular (AV) node

☐ C The left vagus slows conduction through the AV node

☐ D The sympathetic fibres synapse in the stellate ganglion

☐ E The effect of the sympathetic nervous system is of slower but longer duration than the parasympathetic nervous system

**3.141 Regarding the cranial nerves:**

☐ A The trigeminal nerve originates solely in the medulla

☐ B The trigeminal nerve has four autonomic ganglia

☐ C The nasociliary nerve is a branch of the maxillary nerve

☐ D The optic nerve is purely sensory

☐ E The mandibular nerve exits the skull through the foramen rotundum

Anatomy MCQs

**3.140 Answers:**

- A True
- B False
- C True
- D True
- E True

Both parasympathetic and sympathetic nervous systems originate in the cardiovascular control centre in the medulla.

The right vagus acts mainly on the sinoatrial (SA) node.

The nodes are rich in cholinesterase and so deactivate the vagal effect quickly.

Norepinephrine has a slow onset of action but is not metabolised so quickly and therefore has a longer duration of action.

**3.141 Answers:**

- A False
- B True
- C False
- D True
- E False

The trigeminal nerve is the largest cranial nerve.

The motor nucleus is in the upper pons and the sensory nuclei are situated in the midbrain, pons and spinal tract.

The nasociliary nerve is a branch of the ophthalmic nerve, as are the frontal and lacrimal nerves.

The mandibular nerve exits the skull via the foramen ovale.

The maxillary nerve is purely sensory and exits the skull via the foramen rotundum. The ophthalmic nerve exits via the superior orbital fissure.

Reference: Andreas Erdmann. *Concise Anatomy for Anaesthetists.* Cambridge University Press, 2001.

**3.142 Regarding the cranial nerves:**

☐ A The eighth cranial nerve can be affected by tumours at the cerebellopontine angle

☐ B The glossopharyngeal nerve leaves the skull via the foramen magnum

☐ C The glossopharyngeal nerve can be damaged during central venous cannulation of the internal jugular

☐ D The glossopharyngeal nerve supplies the carotid body receptors

☐ E The vagus nerve gives off the recurrent laryngeal nerve on the right but not on the left

**3.142 Answers:**

- A True
- B False
- C True
- D True
- E False

The vestibulocochlear (eighth nerve) originates from the cerebellopontine angle and can therefore easily be affected by lesions in this area.

The glossopharyngeal, vagus and accessory nerves leave the skull via the jugular foramen.

Both vagus and glossopharyngeal nerves are in danger of being damaged during internal cannulation, as they lie between the internal jugular vein and the internal carotid artery.

The glossopharyngeal nerve supplies many structures, including the carotid sinus and body.

The vagus gives off the recurrent laryngeal nerve bilaterally, but the route that it takes is slightly different on each side.

Reference: Andreas Erdmann. *Concise Anatomy for Anaesthetists.* Cambridge University Press, 2001.

**3.143   Regarding lhe larynx:**

☐ A   The hyoid bone is at the level of C3

☐ B   The external branch of the superior laryngeal nerve supplies motor to the cricothyroid muscle

☐ C   The superior laryngeal nerve is a branch of the recurrent laryngeal nerve

☐ D   The laryngeal arterial supply is derived from branches of the thyroid arteries

☐ E   Sensation to the airway below the cords is supplied by the recurrent laryngeal nerve

**3.143  Answers:**

- A  True
- B  True
- C  False
- D  True
- E  True

The vagus gives off both the superior laryngeal and the recurrent laryngeal nerve.

The superior laryngeal nerve gives off two branches: the external and internal laryngeal nerve. The external laryngeal nerves supply motor to the cricothyroid.

The internal laryngeal nerves supply sensation above the vocal cords and to the interior surface of the epiglottis.

The recurrent laryngeal nerve supplies all intrinsic motor muscles of the larynx (with the exception of the cricothyroid) and sensation below the vocal cords.

Reference: Andreas Erdmann. *Concise Anatomy for Anaesthetists.* Cambridge University Press, 2001.

**3.144  Regarding the effects of laryngeal nerve damage:**

☐  A  Partial recurrent laryngeal nerve palsy affects the adductors more than the abductors

☐  B  Superior laryngeal nerve damage leads to a slackening of the cords

☐  C  Complete bilateral recurrent laryngeal nerve damage causes loss of voice

☐  D  Unilateral complete recurrent laryngeal nerve damage causes loss of voice

☐  E  Cords are held midway between the midline and abducted position in complete laryngeal nerve damage

**3.145  Regarding the bronchial tree and lungs:**

☐  A  The trachea bifurcates at the level of T6

☐  B  The right main bronchus is longer than the left

☐  C  The right lower lobe has six segmental bronchi

☐  D  The apex of the lung lies at the level of the clavicles

☐  E  The horizontal fissure follows the line from the fourth costochondral junction to meet the oblique fissure

**3.144  Answers:**

- A  False
- B  True
- C  True
- D  False
- E  True

A partial recurrent laryngeal nerve damage affects abductors more than adductors. This is Semon's law.

Complete unilateral recurrent laryngeal nerve damage does not cause loss of voice because the contralateral cord may move across and restore the voice.

The following voice changes may be heard:

| | |
|---|---|
| Superior laryngeal nerve damage | Weak voice |
| Partial recurrent laryngeal nerve damage | Hoarse voice |
| Complete bilateral recurrent laryngeal nerve damage | Voice lost |

Reference: Yentis SM, Hirsch NP and Smith GB. *Anaesthesia and intensive care A–Z*. An encyclopaedia of principles and practice. 3rd edn. Butterworth Heinemann 2004.

**3.145  Answers:**

- A  False
- B  False
- C  False
- D  False
- E  True

The tracheal bifurcation is at the level of T4.

The right main bronchus is shorter than the left, giving off the right upper bronchus after only 2.5 cm.

Both left and right lower lobes have five segmental bronchi: superior, medial basal, lateral basal, anterior basal and posterior basal.

The apex of the lung lies 4 cm above the clavicle, rendering it vulnerable to puncture during central venous cannulation.

Reference: Erdman A.G. *Concise Anatomy for Anaesthesia*, Cambridge University Press, 2001.

**3.146  Regarding the autonomic nerve system:**

☐  A  The cranial parasympathetic innervation is via cranial nerves II, VII, IX and X

☐  B  The ninth cranial nerve innervates the otic ganglion

☐  C  Sympathetic innervation to pelvic organs is via lumbar nerve routes

☐  D  The cell bodies of the sympathetic system are found in the lateral horn of the spinal cord

☐  E  Postganglionic sympathetic fibres are shorter than postganglionic parasympathetic fibres

**3.147  Regarding peripheral nerves:**

☐  A  The plantar nerve is a branch of the tibial nerve

☐  B  The sural nerve is a direct branch of the sciatic nerve

☐  C  The sural nerve innervates the medial aspect of the foot

☐  D  Posterior cutaneous nerve of the thigh is formed from S3–4 nerve routes

☐  E  The lower lateral cutaneous nerve of the arm is a branch of the radial nerve

**3.146 Answers:**

- A False
- B True
- C True
- D True
- E False

Cranial parasympathetic innervation is via cranial nerves III, VII, IX and X.

The sympathetic innervation to the pelvic organs is via the lumbar routes and the inferior mesenteric ganglion.

Parasympathetic innervation is via sacral routes II–IV.

The postganglionic sympathetic fibres (grey rami communicantes) are longer than the postganglionic parasympathetic as the sympathetic cell bodies do not lie close to the end organs.

Reference: Andreas Erdmann. *Concise Anatomy for Anaesthetists.* Cambridge University Press, 2001.

**3.147 Answers:**

- A True
- B False
- C False
- D False
- E True

The sciatic nerve gives rise to the tibial nerve, which in turn branches to form the sural and plantar nerves.

The sural nerve travels laterally to innervate the lateral aspect of the foot.

The posterior cutaneous nerve of the thigh originates from S1, -2 and -3 (predominantly S2).

Reference: Erdman A.G. *Concise Anatomy for Anaesthesia,* Cambridge University Press, 2001.

**3.148  Regarding the nerves of the brachial plexus:**

☐  A  The upper trunk is formed from C5, C6 and C7

☐  B  The divisions cross the posterior triangle of the neck

☐  C  The cords are named according to their position around the axillary artery

☐  D  The medial cutaneous nerve of the forearm originates from the posterior cord

☐  E  The ulnar nerve is formed from the medial cord

**3.148 Answers:**

- A False
- B False
- C True
- D False
- E True

The best way to answer questions about the brachial plexus is to draw it.

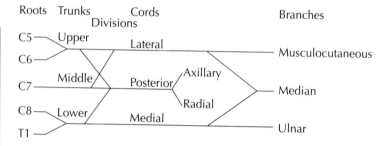

Figure: Brachial plexus

The upper trunk is supplied by C5 and C6. The roots lie in the interscalene groove, the trunks cross over the posterior triangle of the neck and first rib, and the divisions occur behind the clavicle, giving rise to the cords in the axilla. The branches arise at different levels. The medial cutaneous nerve of forearm is a branch of the medial cord.

**3.149 Regarding sacral anatomy:**

☐ A The sacrum is formed from five fused sacral vertebrae

☐ B The unfused fifth sacral lamina forms the sacral hiatus

☐ C The sacral hiatus is covered by the coccygeal membrane

☐ D The sacral canal contains CSF

☐ E Obliteration of the sacral canal would not be a reason for a failed caudal

**3.149 Answers:**

- A True
- B True
- C False
- D True
- E False

The sacrum is formed from the five fused sacral vertebra. Superiorly it articulates with the fifth lumbar vertebra, inferiorly with the coccyx and laterally with innominate bone. The unfused fifth sacral vertebra forms the sacral hiatus. This is bound superiorly by the fused fourth sacral lamina, inferiorly by the posterior body of S5 and laterally by the unfused fifth lamina. It is covered by the sacrococcygeal ligament. The sacral canal contains the dura (including CSF) which usually terminates at the second sacral vertebra on a line joining the posterosuperior iliac spines. It also contains the cauda equina, filum terminale, meninges, sacral and coccygeal nerves, and epidural vasculature. There are a number of reasons for a failed caudal including obliteration of the sacral canal and calcification of the sacrococcygeal ligament.

Reference: Sacrum and sacral hiatus. *Anaesthesia and Intensive Care Medicine* 2002; 3: 435–6.

**3.150 Regarding the diaphragm:**

☐ A  Its nerve supply passes posterior to scalenus anterior

☐ B  Its movement accounts for 50% of the total tidal volume of ventilation

☐ C  The opening for the inferior vena cava is at T10

☐ D  The vagus nerve passes through the diaphragm with the aorta

☐ E  All sensory innervation to the diaphragm is via C3, C4 and C5

**3.150 Answers:**

- A  False
- B  False
- C  False
- D  False
- E  False

The motor innervation for the diaphragm is via C3–5, which pass anterior to scalenus anterior. It also supplies proprioception to the diaphragm. The peripheral parts of the diaphragm receive their sensory innervation from the lower thoracic nerves. Movement of the diaphragm accounts for up to 75% of total tidal volume ventilation. There are three openings in the diaphragm.

| Structure | Level |
| --- | --- |
| Inferior vena cava | T8 |
| Oesophagus | T10 |
| Vagus | T10 |
| Oesophageal branches of left gastric vessels | T10 |
| Aorta | T12 |
| Thoracic duct | T12 |
| Azygos vein | T12 |

Reference: Diaphragm. *Anaesthesia and Intensive Care Medicine* 2005; 6: 301–2.

# CORE TEXT REFERENCES

West JB, *Respiratory Physiology. The Essentials*. 6th edn. Lippincott, Williams & WIlkins 2001.

Power I, Kam P. *Principles of Physiology for the Anaesthetist*. Hodder Arnold 2001.

Yentis SM, Hirsch NP and Smith GB. *Anaesthesia and Intensive Care A–Z. An encyclopaedia of principles and practice*. 3rd edn. Butterworth Heinemann 2004.

# INDEX

Locators in bold refer to book number, those in normal type refer to question number.

Index

Index

Index

Index

221

Index

Index